A Collectors G

CW00944983

MYTH AND MAGIC

John Hughes
and Chris Wotton

Published in the United Kingdom
by
Collectables Publishing Limited

ACKNOWLEDGMENTS

This book would not have been possible without the extensive coop-eration of The Tudor Mint and everyone involved in creating *Myth and Magic*. Thanks especially to Graham Hughes, who allowed us complete freedom to come and go during our research, gave over his showroom as an office, and allowed us to reproduce material copyright to W.A.P. Watson Limited. Thanks to Allan Frost for reading the manuscript, excellent advice and permission to reproduce some of his pho-tographs. Thanks to all the *Myth and Magic* collectors who provided information or helped in other ways (especially Julie Miller and Leigh Whittle), and to everyone at The Tudor Mint for answering our ques-tions: Ian Carey, Helen Coventry, Malcolm Crewdson, Steve Darnley, Roger Gibbons, Heather Lavender, Mark Locker, Stephanie Osborne, Jackie Pielow, Richard Power, Sharon Riley, Anthony Slocombe, Jessica Watson, Lynne Woodward. Thanks to Glenn Blackman for original pho-tography and design.

Front cover picture: The Dragon of Darkness, designed by Jessica Watson and sculpted by Anthony Slocombe.

ISBN 0 9522155 2 7

© Collectables Publishing Limited 1994
3 East Street, Littlehampton,
West Sussex, BN17 6AU England
Telephone: (0903) 733199 Fax: (0903) 733244

Produced by Creativehouse, Aldershot.

Introduction

In 1988, Graham Hughes, Managing Director of The Tudor Mint in Solihull, West Midlands, was looking around for something new. His company's main giftware range — *Crystalflame* — had sold well for a number of years; but interest was beginning to wane, belts were being tightened by all and sundry, and a good idea was badly needed.

Almost by chance, as a result of a lunchtime conversation with a business colleague, he found it. Under the specially created name *Myth and Magic*, and as a test to see if there was a market for such things, a set of twelve pewter figurines of wizards, witches, serpents, castles and demons, each incorporating a full lead crystal, was launched at a trade show in February 1989. They seemed to strike a chord with a wizard and dragon-hungry world, for their popularity was immediate and huge. No sooner had the range first appeared in shops than new orders flowed in. Within the first year staff at The Tudor Mint — and during a recession! — were struggling to keep up with demand. More pieces followed, an extensive range grew, *Myth and Magic* figurines crossed the dividing line from 'giftware' to 'collectable', and the rest (as they say) is history.

Freud, Jung and all the rest of them would no doubt have plenty of theories about it — 'it' being the fascination for so many of a fantasy world inhabited by imaginary folk and mythical creatures. An excess or a lack of gruesome fairy tales when we were young, perhaps . . . who can tell. But as far as the staggering growth in just five years of the market for *Myth and Magic* is concerned, a simpler explanation will suit. Graham Hughes hit on a good idea, he nurtured it well, and the good idea sold.

Mistakes have been made along the way, certainly: 'Evil of Greed' was not the most appealing of names for a piece of giftware; red beads instead of crystals just didn't sell, and (curiously) neither did figurines based upon Greek mythology. Of course, mistakes can be easily rectified, by changing the name, swapping red beads for crystals, or ceasing production of Pipes of Pan, Gorgon Medusa and other poor sellers. Being responsive to the wishes of customers is common sense in the marketplace.

It was this responsiveness that led to the rapid formation of the Myth and Magic Collectors Club — clearly a defining moment. Not only did collectors have a common focal point for their interest, but they were given privileges: advice, news, information and (most importantly) the opportunity to purchase figurines available exclusively to them. They became special.

Then one day, lo and behold, the mistakes along the way — those red beads and Greek tragedies — turn out not to have been mistakes at all! The figurines that nobody wanted are now limited editions, rarities, highly collectable. Suddenly everybody wants them. Demand increases their value (sometimes dramatically) and they change hands between collectors and dealers for considerably more than the original selling price. This is the 'secondary market', which in turn enhances the collectability of the *Myth and Magic* range in general.

Which is where this book comes in. The Tudor Mint's concern is the 'primary market': creating new *Myth and Magic* studies and supplying them to shops for customers to purchase. The secondary market must develop independently, and *A Collectors Guide to Myth and Magic* offers what The Tudor Mint cannot — prices and valuations.

But this book much more than just a price guide. It is a complete reference guide to The Tudor Mint in the 1990s, with facts about and illustrations of every study ever released under the *Myth and Magic*, *Dark Secrets*, *Fantasy and Legend*, *Lord of the Rings* and *Hobbit* headings up until Summer 1994, plus associated products such as jewellery and other memorabilia. It has been compiled with The Tudor Mint's full cooperation in all aspects of factual information — with one exception. The secondary market prices were researched entirely by us, from talking to collectors and dealers world wide.

This book won't tell you whether you should buy or sell a study, but it will tell you how much it tends to fetch on the secondary market. It won't tell you whether one study is better than another, but it will tell you about its history. It won't tell you what's to be retired next year, but it will tell you what's been retired up until now, and which pieces are the rarest . . . and why. Most of all it won't tell you what makes a good collection — because, you, the collector, are the only one who can tell that. The cleverest collector is not the one who buys an 'arm up' Giant Sorceror because it is cheap and sells it at a whacking profit; the cleverest collector is the one who bought it at the retail price in a shop because it appealed to him.

This is an exciting time to be a collector of *Myth and Magic*, and we hope that our Collectors Guide will do much to dispel the myth and enhance the magic. Happy collecting!

John Hughes and Chris Wotton
July 1994

About the Authors

John Hughes was born in 1956 and spent his youth in the English Midlands. He trained as a classical musician and worked in music retailing for a number of years. His interest in collectables began in 1985 when he joined John Hine Studios, initially to help develop a music recording branch of the company. But he soon found himself side-stepping into the world of David Winter Cottages and from 1987 onwards was immersed full-time in developing and running their Collectors Guild. He first discoved *Myth and Magic* when his daughter Alice was given The Guardian Dragon as a christening present by her godfather in 1992. John left David Winter Cottages in 1993 and, together with Heather Lavender, established Collectables Publishing Limited (CPL). *A Collectors Guide to Myth and Magic* is his fifth book and the second in CPL's range of price guides for collectables. He now lives in Surrey with his wife, Chris, and daughters, Helen and Alice.

Chris Wotton was born in Berkshire, England, in 1961. After leaving school he worked for a variety of large companies, before deciding at the age of 24 to concentrate on Information Technology. He spent five years in this industry, finally as a consultant. In 1991 he decided to take three years off to study English and Philosophy at Southampton University. It was during this time that he cultivated a growing interest in the antiques and collectables world and in 1993 he helped to establish Collectables Limited, a retail company specialising in the worldwide sales of collectables. In so doing he developed an in-depth knowledge of *Myth and Magic* in particular. Now 32, Chris spends his time between research work, Collectables Limited, and his cottage near Chichester in West Sussex. He is a keen animal supporter and will be donating a portion of the profits from sales of this book (his first) to the R.S.P.C.A.

C o n t e n t s

Acknowledgments ii
Introduction iii
About the Authors iv
Contents v

Section One
THE MYTH AND MAGIC STORY 6
COLLECTING MYTH AND MAGIC 10

Section Two
MYTH AND MAGIC
CURRENT STUDIES
   Standard Size 18
   Larger 41
RETIRED PIECES 51
   Standard Size 51
   Larger 63
THE COLLECTORS CLUB 67
Crystals and Beads 74
LIMITED AVAILABILITY
   One Year Only Studies 75
   Extravaganza Studies 77
   Exhibition Only Studies 79
OTHER COLLECTIONS
   J.R.R. Tolkien Collections 81
     (The Hobbit & The Lord of the Rings)
   The Arthurian Legend 93
   Dark Secrets 98

Section Three
RARE AND UNRELEASED STUDIES 106
MEMORABILIA 113
JEWELLERY 123
PRICES
   First Issue/1994 List Prices of Current Studies 128
   Secondary Market Price Guide 132
CHECKLIST 136
SOME USEFUL ADDRESSES 140
INDEX 141

The Myth and Magic Story

Birmingham, at the heart of the English Midlands, has long been a centre of great commercial enterprise, with a reputation primarily for heavy industry dating back more than two centuries to the early years of the Industrial Revolution. But England's second city is also home to a number of smaller and lesser-known skills and crafts — it's gunsmiths are the finest in the country, for example. Jewellers, too, have lived and worked there for many generations, producing fine-quality, detailed work. One such craftsman was Walter Archibald Parker Watson, who at the turn of the century ran his own business as a sole trader in Hockley, Birmingham's Jewellery Quarter.

In 1915, Watson sold the business to two partners, A. H. Power and C. Flint, who kept his name when they were establishing their new company — W.A.P. Watson Limited — presumably to retain the reputation he had established over a number of years. Power and Flint originally produced costume jewellery, and this remained the company's prime output for more than half a century, under the trade name *Exquisite Jewellery*. The business did well, expanding gradually over a period of time and requiring a number of moves to larger premises, all within the Jewellery Quarter. In due course Power's two sons, Wallace and Jack, took over the running of what had by then become established as their family business. (In 1994, two members of the family are still directors of the company; one of them, Richard Power, is actively involved in its running.)

Expansion brought interest in new markets, notably crested souvenirs. A 1935 price list includes ash trays, condiments sets, sweet dishes, cake stands, loving cups and butter knives, plus collectors' keepsakes such as paper knives and spoons. The *Exquisite* name was also applied to the souvenirs and other products.

During the Second World War, the company's workshops were turned over to essential war production, its craftsmen's skills placing them in demand to make small and precision components. Percussion caps and parts of Wellington bombers were now their output, with souvenir ash trays made before the war used to store them.

When peace time production resumed in 1945, W.A.P. Watson Limited returned to their successful costume jewellery and souvenir markets. Further expansion was soon required and the decision made to move out of the Jewellery Quarter entirely, due to lack of available space. Solihull, to the south of Birmingham, was chosen as the site of the new premises as it was closer to the homes of both Wallace and Jack Power.

In 1954 the company moved lock, stock and barrel to the 3-acre site in Vulcan Road which it still occupies today. In the 1950s and 60's, with room now to develop, W.A.P. Watson Ltd. became the second largest manufacturer of costume jewellery in the United Kingdom, whilst still retaining a healthy interest in both souvenirs and giftware, the latter under the trade name *Mirella* (mirrors, picture frames, pens, pill boxes etc.)

Graham Hughes (pictured above) — an accountant by training and a local man, born and bred in Solihull — joined W.A.P. Watson Ltd on 1st November 1970 as Company Secretary, at a time when business was thriving and *Exquisite Jewellery* was at the peak of its success. But an unforeseeable problem lay ahead which was to undermine dramatically the demand for domestic costume jewellery — the arrival of cheap imports. They began to hit British manufacturers hard in 1977 and continued to do so into the early 1980s. This decline could have been a far more serious concern for the company than it

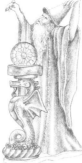

Far Left: One of the Victorian street scenes produced by The Tudor Mint prior to *Myth and Magic*. Left: It all began with this drawing — Sharon Riley's design for The Incantation, dated and signed on an Exquisite Jewellery production card.

turned out to be, had it not (by chance) coincided with a rapid expansion in the souvenir industry — due to a general increase in leisure time, the growth of tourism in the U.K., and a number of momentous special occasions such as the Silver Jubilee (1977) and the Royal Wedding (1981).

The production figures speak for themselves. In the early 1970s the output of W.A.P. Watson Ltd. comprised 60% jewellery, 20% souvenirs and 20% giftware. By 1981 it had changed to 90% souvenirs and just 10% other products.

Relatively speaking these were lean times, with part of the factory closed down and new ideas required to adapt to a changing marketplace. A wide range of products were tried and tested, including leatherware, thimbles, named plaster souvenirs and pewter Victorian street scenes. For the latter, Graham Hughes devised the name 'Tudor Mint', in order to create a quality base upon which to reestablish the giftware side of the business. With such a diversity of interests, changes were also made to the company's structure: The Watson Group Limited was created as a holding company, with W.A.P. Watson Limited being the trading company (hence "WAPW ©" on the nameplate of all *Myth and Magic* studies).

Crystals were first used by the company in the *Exquisite Jewellery* collection, and the idea was developed further with *Crystalflame*, a range of silver and gilt-plated animals, each incorporating a crystal. Although a successful product for The Tudor Mint during the 1980s, *Crystalflame* had clearly peaked in popularity by 1988, and Graham Hughes realised that a new giftware range was badly needed to take its place. The problem was foremost in his mind

when he sat down to lunch one day with an American distributor in New York. Possible solutions entered the conversation, during the course of which a chance suggestion was made: "How about a range based on mythology . . . wizards and dragons and the like?"

The idea appealed, and back in England Graham discussed it further with his Sales Manager, George Atkinson, who thought it had great possibilities. The Tudor Mint's Chief Designer, Sharon Riley, was then briefed to "submit drawings of a collection of dragons, wizards, castles and mythical creatures, to be manufactured incorporating crystals." She researched the subjects thoroughly and in due course presented twenty-five original designs, twelve of which were selected for modelling by Chief Model Maker Roger Gibbons. (The other designs were also later absorbed into the collection.)

Meanwhile, George Atkinson came up with a name for the new collection — *Myth and Magic*.

The figurines, or 'studies' as The Tudor Mint chose to define them, were first shown at a trade show in Birmingham in February 1989. Reaction from stockists was enthusiastic, but nothing compared to the response of their customers when the studies became available in shops. *Myth and Magic* was an instant success. Two months later another twelve studies were issued, and by the end of the year thirty-eight studies and a selection of eleven miniature versions were for sale throughout the UK.

In December, three studies were withdrawn from production — The Evil of Greed, The Infernal Demon and The Deadly Combat — for the simple reason that they did not sell well. In doing so (and by continuing to

7

'retire' less popular studies) the Tudor Mint sowed the seeds for a secondary market which, five years on, is now flourishing as collectors seek to add rare and discontinued pieces to their collections. Unwittingly, W.A.P. Watson Ltd. had joined the collectables industry.

1990 saw the release of the first 'larger' studies, each supplied with a wooden plinth, whilst the total number of 'standard-size' figurines rose to forty-seven. At the same time, six figurines inspired by the *Arthurian Legend* were also issued under the collection title *Fantasy and Legend*.

As an indicator of just how popular the collection had become in such a short period, May saw the launch of the Myth and Magic Collectors Club, only fifteen months after the product first appeared. By the end of July 3,000 members had been enrolled. With the Club came special pieces available exclusively to members for a restricted period only, thus creating a series of limited edition studies to enhance further the collectability of *Myth and Magic*.

The Club also brought into the limelight Allan Frost, an early convert to the *Myth and Magic* collecting fraternity who offered his services to The Tudor Mint as Editor of the Club newsletter, The Methtintdour Times. An anagram of 'The Tudor Mint', 'Methtintdour' is the name of a mythical land created by Allan for the wizards, dragons and other creatures in the *Myth and Magic* range to inhabit. He has created all the fictional story-lines for the studies and has done a great deal to enhance the fantasy aspect of the collection. As well as editing The Methtintdour Times, he has also written a fantasy novel, *The Stracyl of Unity*, published by The Tudor Mint.

Feedback from collectors showed an overwhelming demand for figurines based on the books of J.R.R. Tolkien. The Tudor Mint duly obliged and *The Hobbit Collection* was launched in January 1991, followed by *The Lord of the Rings Collection* a year later. Like the *Arthurian Legend* series, they are not strictly regarded as *Myth and Magic* studies and were launched under the *Fantasy and Legend* title.

These collections generated pleasant coincidences for some members of The Tudor Mint. As a boy, model maker Anthony Slocombe used to walk to school past the house in Birmingham where J.R.R. Tolkien once lived, and by a park which the author used as the inspiration for one of the scenes in *The Lord of the Rings*. And an even closer connection can be found, as for many years Tolkien's son was a Latin teacher at Solihull School, and one of his pupils was a young Graham Hughes.

With other designers and model makers on board, the *Myth and Magic* range continued to grow, with new releases every six month, Sharon Riley and Jessica Watson creating original designs, Roger Gibbons, Mark Locker and Anthony Slocombe sculpting the master models, Graham Hughes and George Atkinson devising names for the studies, and Graham controlling the way the collection was developing. A milestone was reached in January 1991 when the joint skills of Jessica Watson and Anthony Slocombe were combined to produce a tour-de-force — The Power of the Crystal — the largest (and heaviest!) prestige study to date.

In 1992 George Atkinson left the company, since when Graham Hughes alone has named the studies and controlled all aspects of their marketing. Meanwhile Helen Coventry joined the designers and Steve Darnley arrived as a model maker — thus completing the team which currently pools its skills to create *Myth and Magic*.

During a trip to the USA, Graham Hughes had been impressed by the notion of special one-day events for collectors, and decided to adopt a similar scheme here in the UK. The first *Myth and Magic* 'Extravaganza', held in September 1991, proved extremely popular and is now a regular annual event. Since 1992 a special study, available only on the day of the Extravaganza, has been produced, adding greatly to the attraction for collectors. As an extension of this idea, a series of one day events (about six a year) staged in association with *Myth and Magic* stockists were established in 1993, also with an exclusive study available for purchase only on the day.

With the company's history of souvenirs and jewellery manufacture, it is hardly surprising that a range of additional *Myth and Magic* items has appeared over the years — paper knives, trinket boxes, pendants, brooches, earrings, a chess set, plates not to mention a large selection of 'miniatures', are all now currently available.

Amongst the new releases for January

1993 was The Keeper of the Skulls, depicting a skull held in the palm of a giant hand. Such macabre subject matter was something of a gamble as far as The Tudor Mint was concerned and this sinister piece was expected to be unpopular with collectors familiar with the harmonious world of unicorns and wizards so far established in the collection. But the gamble paid off, collectors loved it, and The Keeper of the Skulls turned out to be the best selling study of 1993. Furthermore, it inspired The Tudor Mint to produce *Dark Secrets* the following year, with its chambers of skulls, demons and skeletons — a collection which runs parallel with, rather than as part of, *Myth and Magic*. (Since *Dark Secrets* was launched, a sign has appeared on an office door at W.A.P Watson: "The Chamber of Computers — requires 4 tokens to enter!")

The success of *Myth and Magic* has eclipsed in sheer volume every other facet of W.A.P. Watson's output, and the company has established itself as a successful manufacturer of quality 'collectables'. Nevertheless The Watson Group, in its Exquisite Souvenir and Giftware guise, continues to produce a wide range of souvenirs, including an extensive selection of silver plated spoons, paper knives, collectors and souvenir bells, walking stick mounts, badges, thimbles, key fobs and leather bookmarks. Since 1991, they have also manufactured fantasy figurines along the lines of *Myth and Magic* for Danbury Mint, including a Lord of the Rings chess set, for direct mail marketing.

The appeal of *Myth and Magic* to the buying public in 1989 was immediate, and five years on people are still buying. In an age of instant consumerism, this begs the question, "How long will it last?" The answer depends upon The Tudor Mint's ability not only to attract new collectors but also to retain a freshness and originality in the studies that will maintain the enthusiasm of existing aficionados. All signs indicate that this comes naturally to the people at The Tudor Mint: they have a willingness to experiment and an interaction of ideas between artists, artisans and business personnel that allows for necessary flexibility. Furthermore, with Managing Director Graham Hughes in control of both creativity and business matters, the Tudor Mint is an accountant-led (as opposed to artist-led) collectables company, and there-

fore enjoys the concomitant stability essential in the 1990s world of collectables.

Summer 1994 saw another innovation — the incorporation into the studies of new crystals, much larger, more colourful and varied in shape than the crystals used so far. This dramatically alters the centre of attention from the figurines proper to the crystal — an interesting move. Whether this becomes the style of *Myth and Magic* for the future remains to be seen. If collectors like them, they'll buy them and the collection will adapt accordingly; if not, then we will no doubt see a return to the traditional use of crystals . . . and the 'new' will become the rare 'collectable' of tomorrow. Either way, it's exciting news for collectors.

Below: The Summoner of Light — released in summer 1994.

Collecting Myth and Magic

This chapter has two functions: firstly, to offer general background information about *Myth and Magic* (and other ranges) and secondly, to give advice about buying and selling rare and retired studies.

HOW THE STUDIES ARE MADE

DESIGN A Myth and Magic study starts life as a pencil drawing by one of The Tudor Mint's three designers — Sharon Riley (Chief Designer), Jessica Watson and Helen Coventry. The idea for a study may be theirs, or it may be suggested by Graham Hughes. Almost invariably, design comes first and a name is chosen later. The designers work together, exchanging ideas and commenting on each other's work, which helps to retain a consistency of design for the recurring characters of the collection. The designers must work with practical as well as aesthetic considerations in mind; their ideas must be capable of being made into models and also avoid production difficulties at a later stage, wherever possible. A good example is size: a study cannot be beyond certain dimensions, or it won't fit into the box (see The Giant Sorceror)!

MODEL MAKING When a completed design has been approved, it is passed on to the Model Making Shop, where there are currently four model makers sculpting *Myth and Magic* — Roger Gibbons (Chief Model Maker), Mark Locker, Anthony Slocombe and Steve Darnley.Their task is to transform a two-dimensional design into a three-dimensional figurine, to the exact scale of the design drawing.

Their raw materials are metal (pewter) and Milliput, a resin similar in texture to putty or clay which hardens rapidly (2-3 hours) at room temperature. Having first made a metal framework called an 'armature', they then mould soft Milliput onto the framework, creating the overall shape of the figurine. Once the Milliput has hardened, the fine detail can be sculpted using jeweller's hand tools.

The figurines are usually sculpted in more than one section, for assembly at a later

stage: because all the studies are cast in moulds, the complex designs of the finished figurines would be impossible to produce in a single mould. The number of sections varies: an average standard-sized study has 3 sections; The Crystal Dragon has 18; The Power of the Crystal has 27!

MOULD MAKING The finished model (or its component parts), together with an engraved nameplate for the study, is passed onto the Master Mould Maker, Malcolm Crewdson, whose responsibility it is to make a master mould which will produce exact copies of the figurine. He does this by placing the original sculpted pieces between two rubber discs, which are then placed in a circular metal container to form a 'pack'. The pack is 'cured' in a press at high temperature and under great pressure; when this is done, the two parts of the mould are separated and the original pieces removed. The spaces remaining are precise mirror-image impressions of the pieces. Channels are cut in the rubber to allow molten metal to flow into the spaces and thus exact copies can be cast. Several copies of the prototype pieces are made (called 'multis') and from these, production moulds can be produced The model is now ready to go into production.

CASTING In the Casting Shop, the two-part rubber moulds are assembled and placed in a spinner which rotates at high speed. Using a ladle, molten white metal is poured from a melting pot into a hole in the centre of the mould and centrifugal force carries it along the channels to form the casts. When the metal has cooled and solidified, the pieces are removed from the mould. Faulty casts are returned to the melting pot, as is excess metal in the channels of the mould.

TRIMMING Each of the cast pieces needs to be cleaned up, or 'trimmed.' Excess slithers of metal are scraped away, seams and sharp edges smoothed down, and all trimmings returned to the melting pot.

SOLDERING The individual castings are then soldered together to create the com-

An example of a soldering variation — The Dragon's Spell with left arm in different positions.

pleted study. Soldering is a skilled task, requiring above all a steady hand. Although solderers are given precise instructions on how to assemble the figurines, slight variations do occur — the position of a hand, for example, or the angle of a crystal mount — which explains minor differences between the studies when they appear in shops.

PLATING, OXIDISATION AND RELIEVING The assembled figurines are suspended in rows on a jig and moved into the Plating Shop where they are given a coating of copper, then nickel and finally silver. This is done by an electroplating process, whereby the studies are dipped into various vats containing chemicals.

When the figurines emerge from the last of the dips, the silver coating shines brilliantly. To create the darkened 'antique' *Myth and Magic* look, they are oxidised by dipping them in a sulphur-based chemical, which results in a complete blackening of the silver plating. Then each figurine is 'relieved' (or 'burnished') by holding the model under a spinning buffer, or polishing pad. The result is the familiar blend of grey, black and silver of the finished studies. As the 'relieving' is done by hand, no two models will ever be identical. (Sometimes brown hair-like strands from the buffers attach themselves to the figurines, as collectors may have noticed.) After 'relieving', the models are dipped in a lacquer solution to prevent the silver plate from tarnishing.

CRYSTALS AND HORNS No Myth and Magic study would be complete without its crystal(s), and these are now glued into place — by hand — on the tiny platforms which model makers sculpt specifically for this purpose. The size and shape of crystals varies on some studies, for a variety of rea-

sons; but that's a subject in its own right . . . read on! Unicorns' horns are also glued into place at this stage; three different lengths are used, and these, too, are sometimes interchanged, subject to availability.

THE DROP TEST The figurine is now complete and is boxed and shrink wrapped for despatch to shops and so on to collectors. But if it is a new study, it must first survive The Drop Test! The boxed model is held at shoulder height and dropped onto the floor eight times — onto each face and corner. The model is then unpacked and examined for breakage. It's the simplest way to see whether a figurine will survive the rigours of delivery. If damage is perceived, the study may need to be modified in some way to strengthen or protect the vulnerable part. If so, it returns to the Model Making Shop — and the whole process begins again . . .

VARIATIONS

Some *Myth and Magic* studies have purposefully been altered by The Tudor Mint since first appearing in stores. This is done by remodelling the originals and altering the moulds from which they are duplicated. In this book, these are classed as Mould Variations. So a new study starts as Mould 1; if it is remodelled, Mould 2 results — and so on. When a change is made, the original version (Mould 1) becomes retired and acquires a secondary market value, effectively as a 'limited edition' of unknown number — even if the Mould 2 version is still currently available.

But there are also other variations which occur as a result of the hand assembly process. It is important to know the differences between 'mould variations' and 'production variations', as the former make a considerable difference to the secondary market value of a study, whereas the latter generally do not (apart from a rarity or novelty value). There is one big exception to this rule. Irrespective of whether a mould has been changed or not, the type of crystal attached to it during the last stage of production can alter its secondary market value dramatically.

MOULD VARIATIONS All known mould variations are itemised in Section Two as part of the information about individual studies. Changes are made for the following reasons:

Left: The Infernal Demon's right arm used to rip the moulds during production, so it was remodelled with the arm lower. Right: The Dragon of the Lake with a cubic crystal.

1) To eradicate production problems: e.g. the original 'arm up' version of The Infernal Demon used to rip the moulds during extraction until the arm was repositioned lower.

2) To strengthen weak points: e.g. the left wing of The Armoured Dragon frequently broke off in transit until it was repositioned. Similarly, an extra wall on The Enchanted Castle protected the two turrets from breakage.

3) For aesthetic reasons: e.g. the addition of jagged walls to The Sorceror's Apprentice, or giving The Dawn of the Dragon a more animated appearance. Sometimes this coincides with strengthing a weak point: the touching heads on Mould 2 of The Dragon's Kiss not only consummates the kiss but also makes the figurine more sturdy.

4) To make the piece fit in the box. The wings on The Deadly Combat were brought together and The Giant Sorceror's arm was lowered for this reason!

5) To rectify sculpting errors or misinterpretations. The wizard gained a missing foot on Mould 2 of The Enchanted Pool; and an embarrassing rock formation was removed from The Flying Dragon.

The Tudor Mint have only recently started keeping records of changes to moulds, and we have had to rely on the (amazing) memories of the modellers and designers to amass our information. But human memory is not infallible and further variations are bound to exist.

CRYSTAL AND BEAD VARIATIONS Over the years a variety of crystal shapes, sizes and colours have been used on *Myth and Magic* figurines — a list can be found on page 74. Consequently examples of the same study can be found with different crystals attached, and if it is an unusual crystal this can affect the secondary market value as much as (or even more than) a mould variation.

Cubes, Cones and Footballs

Cubic and conical crystals were phased out almost entirely in 1992 due to erratic deliveries from The Tudor Mint's supplier. (That's why Excalibur, for example, will appear 99.9% of the time with two 8mm round crystals — and then suddenly turn up with two cubes.) Invariably cubes and cones were replaced by round crystals (more accurately 'globe' crystals). Round crystals with large facets (rather like footballs) also exist. They are as rare as cubes and cones and should not be confused with standard round crystals.

Models with cubic or conical crystals are now sought after, though they appear to matter less to some collectors than others. This subjectivity makes the premium they attract difficult to pinpoint. As a rule of thumb we suggest that a non-standard crystal (i.e. not round) should increase the value of a study by at least £30.

Having said this, beware of over excitement when coming across The Dragon of Wisdom with a conical crystal in your local shop at list price. The Tudor Mint are still producing them that way in 1994.

Colours

All crystals are naturally clear; it is the metal foil behind them which gives them colour. Different foils allow different colours to be reflected. The most common is multicoloured, or rainbow-coloured (actual name: Medium Vitrail); but The Tudor Mint used deep blue (Bermuda Blue) crystals regularly when *Myth and Magic* first began, though now they are much less common. Pinky-blue (Heliotrope) and pale blue (Aquamarine) are still used on some models, but in small quantities; perhaps one in thirty. The rarest of them all is greeny/gold (Sahara), used very rarely and extremely sought-after by serious collectors. (See The Quest for the Truth.)

As with crystal shapes, the value of crystal colours is a subjective matter, compounded by the fact that The Tudor Mint do not keep records of which pieces were issued with which crystals, and therefore quantities are unknown. Before 1992 their point of view was "if we've got it use it — whatever the shape or colour." (Sometimes this applies whether the study has a mount for a particular shaped crystal or not. We have seen circular mounts with cubes on, triangular mounts with conical or round crystals — and every other variation in between!)

Red Beads

A number of studies were produced in 1989 with a red bead instead of a crystal, usually to create a special effect — such as the glowing light in The Old Hag's lantern. But they did not sell well and the beads were replaced by standard round crystals (with slight remodelling of the mount). The red beaded versions of The Old Hag, The Alchemist and The Astronomer are now highly collectable and worth double or treble the value of their crystal counterparts.

OTHER VARIATIONS The following types of variation can be found but are not due to deliberate mould changes.

1) Differences caused by soldering assembly. For example, on The Spirits of the Forest, the unicorn may face different ways, or on The Incantation, the wizard's left arm may be held at different angles.

2) Differences caused by replacing crystal mounts. Over the years the method of holding crystals (on hands, rocks, cauldrons etc.) has been improved, generally by giving them a stronger mount. Thus, for example, The Siren may hold the crystal either in the palm of her hand or on a mount. Although minor variations, 'early' (i.e. non-mount) studies nevertheless attract a premium of between £10 and £20.

3) Differences caused by reducing the number of soldering points when a study is remodelled to be cast as a whole rather than in sections. For example, The Gorgon was originally made in three pieces (the column, the base and the Gorgon herself); but it was later cast as a complete model.

4) Differences caused by nameplate alterations. Early nameplates without a number or with 'GT. BRITAIN' instead of 'UK' will attract a premium of £10-20. (See also The Keeper of the Treasure.)

5) Differences caused by altering the angle of the crystal. In 1990 The Tudor Mint decided to position all multicoloured crystals so they face forwards, to display their rainbow effect from the front. All existing studies were adapted accordingly. Thus, in The Cauldron of Light, for example, the crystal was originally set horizontally into the cauldron; later it was altered to face forwards. 'Flatter-lying' crystals fetch a premium of perhaps £10-20.

6) Differences caused during casting. When pieces are extracted from the mould, they are still hot and remain slightly pliable until they have cooled further. Consequently a wizard's body or a dragon's wings might sit at slightly different angles.

7) The texture of, say, a wizard's cloak or a dragon's wings may vary. Smoother textures result as moulds begin to wear and lose their detail. Also, new textures are sometimes added by the model makers: technically these are mould variations, but so minor that they have not (yet) been documented.

8) Colour variations. The hand 'burnishing' gives infinite variety to the shades of grey, silver and black. Generally speaking, the figurines are darker in the more accessible nooks and crannies where the spinning buffer cannot reach, whilst exposed areas are lighter, particularly edges and flat surfaces.

EDITION SIZES

Apart from pre-announced limited edition studies (e.g. The Dragon Master, The VII Seekers of Knowledge) the edition sizes of Myth and Magic studies and other collections are not made public by The Tudor Mint, which is their prerogative. However, The Methtintdour Times has been known to publish the final edition sizes of Collectors

13

Left: Sauria, the first Extravaganza study; only 403 were issued. Above: Baseplate variations — The White Witch has the earlier 'GT. BRITAIN' marking whilst The Earth Wizard reads 'UK'. Right: An example of a *Fantasy and Legend* baseplate with the jousting knight logo.

Club studies — e.g. The Jovial Wizard (11,679), The Well of Aspirations (2,973), Playmates (3,778) — and keeps tabs on sales of the limited editions studies. Extravaganza study editions are also known: Sauria (403) and Deinos (463). As these figures indicate, restricted availability studies in particular are a worthwhile investment. Occasionally the edition sizes of a Mould 1 version are known (albeit approximately), and these have been quoted in Section Two whenever available.

The largest edition sizes are clearly the studies which have been available for the longest period of time, namely The Incantation and The Siren; both are still selling well after five years. The fastest selling study to date is The Keeper of the Skulls: 25,000 models in the first year of production!

NAMEPLATES

Myth and Magic nameplates (or baseplates, if you prefer) have always included the name of the piece, the sculptor (i.e. model maker) in the form of a signature, and copyright information. (Curiously, designers are never credited.)So the nameplate of the very first model to be made read:

THE INCANTATION
BY
Roger Gibbons
WAPW © GT. BRITAIN

This remained standard until the latter half of 1990, when the last line was changed to WAPW © UK — to make the text fit onto smaller studies easier. At about the same time, it was decided to include code numbers. Nameplates for new studies were engraved accordingly and nameplates of existing studies were modified. However, both changes were not necessarily made at the same time to all models. Thus, it is possible to find early studies with as many as four different variations. For example:

THE INCANTATION BY Roger Gibbons
WAPW © GT. BRITAIN
THE INCANTATION BY Roger Gibbons
WAPW © UK
THE INCANTATION BY Roger Gibbons
WAPW © UK 3001
THE INCANTATION BY Roger Gibbons
WAPW © GT. BRITAIN 3001

Of the four styles, the last is the rarest, as the overlap of GT. BRITAIN with code number was very brief and, according to The Tudor Mint, should not exist at all!

When buying and selling, non-numbered studies and studies marked GT. BRITAIN attract an additional premium of approximately £10. If a study is marked GT. BRITAIN and has a code number, the figure will be more than £10.

On some of the larger studies, nameplate information is situated on a plaque on the actual study itself. Information on baseplates of other collections is standard and typical examples are given at the beginning

14

of each listing in Section Two. Occasionally a study is fitted with the wrong baseplate by mistake: issue 7 of The Methtintdour Times told of a collector in Scotland who has a Smaug with a nameplate that reads 'The Capture of Bilbo'! (*Hobbit* nameplates are a separate disc, and clearly the wrong one had been attached: they also tend to drop out occasionally.)

There is much interplay between model makers and their work, and the name credited on the baseplate of a study does not always reflect the person who sculpted it. For example, it was originally intended that all the *Myth and Magic* figurines would be sculpted by Roger Gibbons, and all the *Fantasy and Legend* were to be by Mark Locker. But in practice whoever was available at the time sculpted the study, whether it was *Fantasy and Legend* or *Myth and Magic*. As baseplates are often engraved in advance, some may credit Roger Gibbons, when in fact they were modelled by Mark Locker (e.g. The Book of Spells, The Cauldron of Light). A more recent example is The Swordmaster. This study is ascribed to Mark Locker on the baseplate — but he had other commitments at the time, and it is in fact the work of Anthony Slocombe.

PROTOYPES

On occasions The Tudor Mint have given away pre-production prototypes as prizes or incentives for renewing Collectors Club membership. Even though they may vary only slightly from the issued study, their rarity makes them highly collectable. Every prototype sent to a collector is supplied with a Certificate of Authenticity.(See individual

The released version of The Dragon of the Moon (left) and the prototype (right) with both feet on the ground.

entries for further details The Wizard of Autumn, The Wizard of Spring, The Dragon of the Moon, The Sun Dragon, The Dragon of the Clouds, The Visionary, Playmates).

BOXES AND PACKAGING

Before they had their own special boxes, *Myth and Magic* studies were sold in the blue boxes, with slide-on lid, used by W.A.P. Watson Ltd. for despatching jewellery; they even had a sticker on which read *Exquisite Jewellery* . Larger studies were supplied in plain brown boxes. This was a 'make-do' situation which was rectified as soon it was clear that the range was here to stay. Needless to say, blue boxes (with the figurine inside, of course) are now collectable!

The familiar scarlet *Myth and Magic* box (large and small) with The Magical Encounter on the lid was first introduced in 1990, together with the customised packaging inside. This has remained standard ever since. However, a new and more sophisticated design is planned for 1995, along the lines of the the artwork on the *Myth and Magic* displays to be seen in some shops.

Other collections (*The Hobbit, Lord of the Rings, Dark Secrets*) have their own customised boxes.

Inside the box, the wooden plinth that accompanies larger studies has normally been placed on top of the model, or underneath it in some cases. In 1994 the packaging was modified so that the plinth slots down the side of the box. (Incidentally, wooden plinths were originally produced abroad; but Graham Hughes adopts a 'Buy British' policy whenever possible, and they are now made by an English supplier.)

THE SECONDARY MARKET

When The Tudor Mint retires a study, production ceases and, once existing stocks have been sold, the piece will no longer be available from their stockists (the primary market). It then effectively becomes a 'limited edition' item of unknown quantity, and invariably increases in value beyond its issue price. This also applies to original mould versions when a study is modified. The only way to purchase the figurine from then onwards is from someone who already owns one, be they a collector or dealer. This additional buying and selling is referred to as the 'secondary market' (not to be confused with the 'grey market', which is entirely different; see next section about 'where to buy'.)

The secondary market in *Myth and Magic* (and other Tudor Mint collections) is still in its infancy but has increased dramatically in the past two years or so. It's a complex business, with prices fluctuating (as in any market) according to supply and demand. The *Myth and Magic* market is further convoluted by the fact that mould, crystal and (to a lesser extent) production variations have to be taken into account as well as straightforward retirements.

As at the summer of 1994, prices are rising rapidly, though the secondary market will undoubtedly stabilise at some point. Hopefully this book will help to achieve this stability sooner rather than later, as a market without guidelines becomes a 'free-for-all' in which there can only be winners and losers. Having said this, our prices are a guide only; for no matter what opinions are expressed and prices quoted, true market values are set by people buying and selling.

Such dealing is carried out independently of The Tudor Mint who, as the manufacturer, maintain (rightly) a policy of non-involvement in the secondary market.

WHERE SHOULD I BUY AND HOW MUCH SHOULD I PAY?

CURRENT FIGURINES Current models are available from The Tudor Mint's extensive network of nominated stockists. The actual price of the figurines may vary from one shop to another, for although The Tudor Mint have issued a recommended price list annually since 1992, stockists are not obliged to adhere strictly to the figures quoted.

The 'grey market' which plagues some collectable manufacturers is not currently a problem for The Tudor Mint, and long may it remain so. The 'grey market' is the practise of 'authorised' (i.e.nominated) stockists selling stocks onto unauthorised stockists — usually in large quantities — so that the product appears for sale elsewhere, usually at discounted prices. This undermines the initial value of the product, and therefore its collectability, and reduces the manufacturer's control over how his product is marketed.

RETIRED FIGURINES There are a number of specialist dealers in retired collectables, most of whom are aware of the current interest in

Myth and Magic. They advertise regularly in appropriate magazines and periodicals, some of which are listed in Section Three. Also, rare studies can still be tracked down in shops at the original list price, with a spot of detective work and a little bit of luck.

Collectors selling studies should bear in mind that a dealer will offer a price lower than the market value — 40% lower on average — but this fluctuates depending on prevailing circumstances, the number of pieces being sold, their condition, and demand for particular studies at the time. The importance of dealers to collectors is that they have good stocks and have excellent contacts to track down specific requirements. In other words, they provide a service.

Exchanges between collectors adhere more to the full market value as a profit margin is not necessarily a prerequisite. However, making contact is the problem here.

TAKING CARE OF YOUR FIGURINES

The safest and cleanest place for your precious studies is in the box. But if you insist on displaying them in your home, here are a few suggestions from The Tudor Mint on how to take care of them:

1) Remove accumulated dust by using a small soft-haired brush. A blusher brush and a baby's toothbrush are ideal.

2) Wipe the crystal gently using a lint-free cloth.

3) Do not use a damp cloth.

4) Do not get the models wet or in contact with abrasive substances, including household and silver cleaner.

5) Do not expose them to direct sunlight or strong artificial light.

6) Do not pick up the models by holding the crystal.

7) Do not place the models near a heat source, such as a radiator or fire.

8) Keep them out of the reach of children.

9) Don't drop them.

Introduction to Listings

The main collection of *Myth and Magic* studies are listed in two groups — Current and Retired — and within the groups, standard-sized studies precede larger studies. These are followed by studies of limited availability — One Year Only, Extravaganza, Exhibition Only — the Collectors Club studies, and finally collections which are related to but not strictly classified as *Myth and Magic* — *The Hobbit, The Lord of the Rings, The Arthurian Legend, Dark Secrets* and *Dinosaurs*.

DESIGNERS AND MODEL MAKERS
The designer and model maker of a study are identified by his or her initials: DESIGNERS: SR = Sharon Riley, JW = Jessica Watson, HC = Helen Coventry. MODEL MAKERS: RG = Roger Gibbons, ML = Mark Locker, AS = Anthony Slocombe, SD = Steve Downley, JP = John Pickering (freelance), M = Member (Collectors Club Member). If a model maker worked on a study uncredited, his initials appear in brackets after the credited model maker.

ISSUE DATES
The Tudor Mint release new products twice a year — winter and summer — and in most cases we have standardized the month of release to January and August. There are some exceptions, however, and these have been noted: for example, the first two groups of *Myth and Magic* studies were released in March and May 1989 respectively; also, the summer 1994 releases were already appearing in shops in July.

ISSUE PRICES
'Issue Price' means the price for which studies sold in shops when they were first released. Regular price increases have been made over the years and in the case of studies still currently available, it's interesting to see how issue prices compare in 1994. As for retired studies, the comparison is even more interesting. (Since 1992 The Tudor Mint have produced retail price lists, and these have been used as the prime reference source. Between 1989 and 1991, however, no such lists existed and issue prices have been calculated from known trade prices; consequently they may vary from actual figures and should be treated as a guide only.)

DIMENSIONS
In all cases, the dimensions of a piece are given in this order: Width x Depth x Height. 'Width' and 'Depth' are measured across the baseplate, and 'Height' from the edge of the baseplate to the top of the model. Sizes of larger studies do not include the wooden plinth.

The following *Myth and Magic* studies were still in production in summer 1994. The list includes studies currently for sale but earmarked for retirement in December 1994. Code numbers for standard-sized studies begin with 3001 (The Incantation) and there are no gaps in the numerical order — so, for example, 3080 (The Leaf Spirit) is the eightieth standard-sized study to be added to the collection. In fact, the numbering of all Tudor Mint's collections is similarly straightforward. However, in the larger *Myth and Magic* series, which begins at 3300, the numbers 3316 and 3317 are mysteriously absent.

Typical *Myth and Magic* base marking: THE DRAGON GATEWAY by Roger Gibbons 3028 WAPW © U.K. (For details of base plate variations, see Collecting Myth and Magic in Section One.)

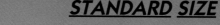

STANDARD SIZE

THE INCANTATION

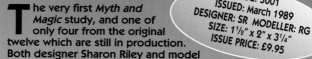

CODE: 3001
ISSUED: March 1989
DESIGNER: SR MODELLER: RG
SIZE: 1½" x 2" x 3¼"
ISSUE PRICE: £9.95

The very first *Myth and Magic* study, and one of only four from the original twelve which are still in production. Both designer Sharon Riley and model maker Roger Gibbons were very excited about the challenge this new collection presented and this is clearly reflected in the freshness of their work. Originally the dragon supporting the crystal was further away from the wizard, but it had a tendency to break off. The study was remodelled so that the dragon was moved back and the wings were made longer, to touch the wizard's cloak. The hands and arms of the wizard do appear at different angles occasionally, due to slight variations in production.

THE SIREN

CODE: 3002
ISSUED: March 1989
DESIGNER: SR MODELLER: RG
SIZE: ⅞" x 1 ⅞" x 3½"
ISSUE PRICE: £9.95

The Siren is the only study from the original twelve which has not had a major remodelling nor been retired. Perhaps the subject matter has something to do with this — the Siren is said to entice people by the sweetness of her song: so beautiful is it that the listener forgets everything else, and dies of hunger! The Siren's right arm has caused the odd soldering problem over the years and as a result varies in position from study to study.

THE BOOK OF SPELLS

CODE: 3004
ISSUED: March 1989
DESIGNER: SR MODELLER: RG (ML)
SIZE: 1¹/₂" x 2" x 3¹/₂"
ISSUE PRICE: £9.95

A wizard that has survived the years since the first issue, although with modifications. On Mould 1, the wizard's left hand tilts backwards, and his right arm extends beyond his cloak sleeve, but as it was prone to break off, the cloak was extended for Mould 2. Despite the credit on the nameplate, this was in fact Mark Locker's first *Myth and Magic* study.

THE CAULDRON OF LIGHT

CODE: 3006
ISSUED: March 1989
DESIGNER: SR MODELLER: ML/RG
SIZE: 1³/₈" x 2 ¹/₄" x 3¹/₂"
ISSUE PRICE: £9.95

T he first issue (actually modelled by Mark Locker) had the stars in the cauldron 'leaping' from the mixture, on jets of magic. Production problems (i.e. the stars tended to snap off) demanded a restyling, with the stars resting in the mixture and a new cauldron (Mould 2). Then, in 1992, Roger Gibbons was asked to produce new moulds for the study — but the original wizard 'master' had gone missing. It was eventually found and a new study produced. Only some months later did people realise that in fact the wrong wizard had been used; not the original 'master' but one originally intended for The Keeper of the Treasure (3046)! And that is why the wizard on Mould 3 has lost much of his beard and has gained a more stylish medallion!

THE GUARDIAN DRAGON

CODE: 3021
ISSUED: May 1989
DESIGNER: SR MODELLER: RG
SIZE: 2" x 1⁷/₈" x 3"
ISSUE PRICE: £9.95

H ard though it is to believe, this was the first 'real' *Myth and Magic* dragon (if you exclude The Winged Serpent and The Deadly Combat). These days there seem to be more dragons than anything else, but it was the popularity of this piece that first alerted the dragon-hungry collectors-in-waiting. In fact, so popular has this figurine been that it is still in production after five years, with only a minor alteration. This affection is shared within the company, where the study is known as *Puff the Magic Dragon*, because of his 'cute' features. In Mould 1 the dragon's horns are long and in Mould 2 they are short.

THE GRIM REAPER

CODE: 3023
ISSUED: May 1989
DESIGNER: SR MODELLER: RG (ML)
SIZE: 1¼" x 1½" x 3½"
ISSUE PRICE: £9.95

This popular figurine is as fine an example as any of how death has its own fascination for collectors. No mould variations exist.

THE UNICORN ▶

CODE: 3024
ISSUED: May 1989
DESIGNER: SR MODELLER: RG
SIZE: 1" x 2 ½" x 3½"
ISSUE PRICE: £9.95

The first of its kind in the *Myth and Magic* range, this study began that occasional occupation familiar to most collectors — sticking the horn back on the unicorn. Two versions exist — in Mould 1 the right foreleg is above the crystal, whilst in Mould 2 it bends behind (the change was made to prevent breakage).

CODE: 3027
ISSUED: August 1989
DESIGNER: SR MODELLER: RG
SIZE: 1¾" x 2 ⅜" x 3"
ISSUE PRICE: £12.95

◀ THE CASTLE OF SOULS

Originally the first of the larger castles had the crystals set lower down in the turrets (Mould 1), but the turrets were then filled in (Mould 2). The 'souls' in question can be seen whining and moaning in the castle walls. This study is particularly effective with conical crystals.

CODE: 3028
ISSUED: August 1989
DESIGNER: SR MODELLER: RG
SIZE: 2¼" x 2 ¼" x 3½"
ISSUE PRICE: £12.95

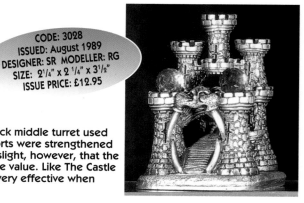

THE DRAGON GATEWAY ▶

In Mould 1 of this study, the back middle turret used to break off, and so the supports were strengthened for Mould 2. The change is so slight, however, that the change does not greatly affect the value. Like The Castle of Souls, The Dragon Gateway is very effective when found with conical crystals.

THE DRAGON RIDER

CODE: 3029
ISSUED: August 1989
DESIGNER: SR MODELLER: RG (ML)
SIZE: 1¼" x 2" x 3½"
ISSUE PRICE: £9.95

The Dragon Rider has had three incarnations. In the first (Mould 1), the rider held the crystal in her right hand; but this would frequently snap off and only 400 were made. In the second (Mould 2), the crystal had moved to her left hand, the dragon had gained reins, and the Rider's cloak was extended to protect her right arm. Currently the crystal is still in the left, but the reins have gone, and the Rider's cloak is more textured (Mould 3). This particular dragon might be described as 'aerodynamically challenged', in view of the fact that he has no wings! Although uncredited, Mark Locker worked on both this and the next study (numerically), The Dragon's Kiss.

THE REBORN DRAGON

CODE: 3033
ISSUED: August 1989
DESIGNER: SR MODELLER: RG
SIZE: 2" x 1½" x 2¼"
ISSUE PRICE: £9.95

In some senses a very rare piece — one which hasn't been restyled at all since inception!

CODE: 3036
ISSUED: August 1989
DESIGNER: SR MODELLER: RG
SIZE: 1½" x 2¾" x 3¾"
ISSUE PRICE: £9.95

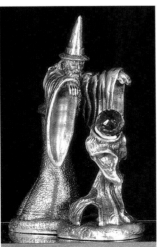

THE WIZARD OF LIGHT

One of the two close advisors to the Giant Sorceror, The Wizard of Light is guardian of the light of all knowledge and is seen here casting a spell. Originally the Wizard had very long hands which used to break off quite easily (Mould 1), so Roger Gibbons remodelled the piece with longer sleeves and shorter hands (he also moved the knarled tree supporting the crystal closer to the wizard) (Mould 2). Unfortunately, during all this excitement, Roger forgot to replace the sash decorating the right hand side of his cloak. Now models with the sash are quite sought after. Usually, a new study is modelled first and then named later; but in the case of The Wizard of Light, the name came first.

PEGASUS

CODE: 3038
ISSUED: August 1989
DESIGNER: SR MODELLER: RG
SIZE: ³/₄" x 2¹/₂" x 3¹/₂"
ISSUE PRICE: £9.95

This is the first appearance in the collection of Pegasus, the flying horse on which Bellerophon attempted to ride to Heaven. The original version of the study had a long tail (Mould 1) but this was shortened for the model in current production (Mould 2). It would be romantic to imagine that the tail was shortened to aid Pegasus' ability to fly on such a long and perilous quest. Actually it was to stop his back legs bending.

THE FIRE WIZARD

Although part of the Elemental Wizards group, this study was not retired along with the others in December 1991 as it was much more popular with collectors in its own right. It is most sought-after with a cubic crystal. SCHEDULED FOR RETIREMENT: 31st December 1994.

CODE: 3040
ISSUED: January 1990
DESIGNER: SR MODELLER: RG
SIZE: 1¹/₂" x 2" x 3³/₄"
ISSUE PRICE: £10.95

MOTHER NATURE ▼

Interesting bit of trivia . . . Mother Nature was the first female to appear for over a year. She has remained popular, and is one of the three survivors from the January 1990 issue. Sharon Riley imagines Mother Nature as a fairy dancing amongst flowers — hence the wings (which, incidentally, are pressed, not cast in a mould like most other components). Prior to April 1994 the setting for the crystal was shallower and it tended to fall out occasionally (Mould 1). The setting was then deepened (Mould 2).

CODE: 3043
ISSUED: January 1990
DESIGNER: SR MODELLER: RG
SIZE: 1¹/₂" x 1¹/₄" x 3³/₄"
ISSUE PRICE: £10.95

Designer Profile

SHARON RILEY
(Chief Designer)

Sharon Riley joined W.A.P. Watson Ltd. as a designer in 1983 and apart from an 'O' level in Art is entirely self-taught as an artist. In the past decade she has worked on all aspects of the company's output and was responsible for the first twelve *Myth and Magic* designs launched in early 1989. Since then she has generated more ideas for studies than any other designer. Her favourite models are The Dragon of the Underworld and Dactrius as she likes the effect of dragons coiling themselves around objects. Sharon's son, Daniel (aged 3), was born around the time she designed the Collectors Club study Playmates — hence the little cherub on the piece. Sometimes Graham Hughes attempts to draw ideas for new studies himself, and Sharon is usually the one who is given the job of deciphering them!

CODE: 3046
ISSUED: January 1990
DESIGNER: SR MODELLER: RG
SIZE: 2 ½" x 1 ½" x 3 ½"
ISSUE PRICE: £10.95

THE KEEPER OF THE TREASURE

Due to an oversight during production, the first pieces were released with no designer's signature on the baseplate (Mould 1), and they are now very sought-after. The Keeper of the Treasure was introduced as a replacement for The Evil of Greed (3003). In the model making workshop, the wizard of this study somehow got mixed up with the wizard from The Cauldron of Light (3006) — thus the two tend to look rather similar.

CODE: 3049
ISSUED: August 1990
DESIGNER: SR MODELLER: RG
SIZE: 2⅝" x 1¾" x 3¼"
ISSUE PRICE: £10.95

THE DRAGON OF THE FOREST

The dragon is shown holding the Crystal of Perpetual Light, which guides travellers through his forest. Like The Dragon of the Sea (3048), he too has a relative on The Dragon Master (3300). SCHEDULED FOR RETIREMENT: 31st December 1994.

CODE: 3050
ISSUED: August 1990
DESIGNER: SR MODELLER: RG
SIZE: 3¼" x 2 ¼" x 3"
ISSUE PRICE: £10.95

THE DRAGON OF WISDOM

Known to some collectors as 'Norman', The Dragon of Wisdom frequently appears with a cubic crystal, which fetches a premium. This dragon has a doppelganger on The Dragon Master (see also 3048 and 3049). He is also one of Allan Frost's favourite studies — especially if it has a cubic crystal! — and was the inspiration behind Tomepicker in his novel The Stracyl of Unity. (Got it yet? Norman . . . Wisdom?)

SPIRITS OF THE FOREST

CODE: 3051
ISSUED: August 1990
DESIGNER: SR MODELLER: RG
SIZE: 3¹/₂" x 1³/₄" x 3"
ISSUE PRICE: £10.95

The Unicorn (3024) had continued to be popular since its appearance in mid-1989, and collectors' appetites were further rewarded by the issue of both this study and 3052, Virgin and Unicorn. The name 'Spirits of the Forest' comes from Chinese unicorn mythology. The study does not depict a mother and foal, as one might imagine, unicorns being asexual. One variation is known, but only as an accident. A new member of The Tudor Mint's soldering department assembled a batch with the smaller unicorn the wrong way round — until he was told of his mistake! A model like this was sold in 1993 for £125.

THE WIZARD OF AUTUMN

The wizards that make up the 'seasons set' have remained popular since issue. The prototype wizard is slightly larger, with a long staff, and six were offered to

CODE: 3053
ISSUED: January 1991
DESIGNER: JW MODELLER: RG
SIZE: 2¹/₄" x 1¹/₂" x 3¹/₂"
ISSUE PRICE: £12.95

randomly-chosen members as an incentive to rejoin the Collectors Club in Spring 1991 (see also 3055, 3057, 3058, 3059, 3075). Prototypes were supplied with a Certificate of Authenticity. This was Jessica Watson's first study; the finished model turned out very similar to her design, although her drawing was slightly larger and the wizard's cloak was shorter (it was lengthened as it tended to break in the 'drop test' — see 'How *Myth and Magic* are made' in Section One).

THE WIZARD OF WINTER

CODE: 3054
ISSUED: January 1991
DESIGNER: JW MODELLER: RG
SIZE: 2" x 1³/₄" x 3¹/₄"
ISSUE PRICE: £12.95

All of the 'seasons set' were designed by Jessica Watson, and it is to her credit that the figurines look as fresh and appealing to collectors as they did back in 1991 — indeed only one study has been retired. The Wizard of Winter gives the feeling of austerity and barrenness. Two versions exist, though the difference is small. In Mould 1 the icicles behind the wizard's head were longer, but as these tended to snap off they were toned down shortly after release.

THE WIZARD OF SPRING ▶

CODE: 3055
ISSUED: January 1991
DESIGNER: JW MODELLER: AS
SIZE: 2³/₈" x 1¹/₂" x 3"
ISSUE PRICE: £12.95

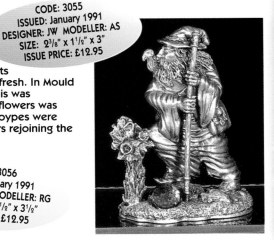

The study is indeed spring-like with its theme of renewal and setting out afresh. In Mould 1 the wizard's hat has a 'bobble'; this was removed for Mould 2, and the clump of flowers was extended slightly. As with 3053, six protoypes were given away to randomly-chosen members rejoining the Collectors Club.

CODE: 3056
ISSUED: January 1991
DESIGNER: JW MODELLER: RG
SIZE: 2¹/₈" x 1¹/₂" x 3¹/₂"
ISSUE PRICE: £12.95

THE WIZARD OF SUMMER

Like The Wizard of Autumn (3053), a small number (thirty) of the Collectors Club members received the certificated prototype of this study as a prize when they were selected from subscription renewals in 1991. In fact the difference between prototype and issued model is tiny — one flower is slightly altered.

CODE: 3057
ISSUED: January 1991
DESIGNER: JW MODELLER: RG
SIZE: 2¹/₂" x 1³/₄" x 3¹/₂"
ISSUE PRICE: £12.95

THE DRAGON OF THE MOON

The prototype of this dragon, which was offered as a prize in a draw, is slightly taller and wider that that eventually issued, and his feet were both on the ground. This tended to give the appearance that the dragon was 'answering a call of nature' — so his left leg was raised up onto a rock.

Current Pieces

THE SUN DRAGON

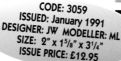

CODE: 3058
ISSUED: January 1991
DESIGNER: JW MODELLER: ML
SIZE: 2¾" x 2" x 2¾"
ISSUE PRICE: £12.95

About 325 pieces exist with the 'proper' title 'Dragon of the Sun' (Mould 1). However, early in the life of this study, its baseplate was mislaid and a new one was cast bearing the title 'The Sun Dragon' (as the piece had become known at The Tudor Mint studios). All pieces are now released as 'The Sun Dragon' (Mould 2). A prototype exists with the dragon sniffing the flower, rather than appearing to eat it, and without a ruff.

THE DRAGON OF THE CLOUDS

On the issued study, the dragon's feet 'sit' on the cloud; but a protoype exists (never released), slightly taller, with the feet raised above the cloud, and smaller wings. Both this study and The Dragon of the Sun were the first to be released as officially sculpted by Mark Locker (though he had worked on earlier studies uncredited).

CODE: 3059
ISSUED: January 1991
DESIGNER: JW MODELLER: ML
SIZE: 2" x 1⅝" x 3¼"
ISSUE PRICE: £12.95

THE SPIRITED PEGASUS

The second Pegasus figurine in the collection has continued the popularity of the first (3038). Here he is seen flying over clouds. SCHEDULED FOR RETIREMENT: 31st December 1994.

CODE: 3060
ISSUED: January 1991
DESIGNER: JW MODELLER: RG
SIZE: 3" x 1¼" x 2¾"
ISSUE PRICE: £12.95

Designer Profile

JESSICA WATSON

Jessica Watson (no relation to W.A.P. Watson) studied at Birmingham University and gained a first class BA Degree in Fine Arts. She originally joined the company in 1987 and, amongst other things, worked on designs for bookmarks and Crystalflame before taking two years off during which time she obtained a Post Graduate Certificate of Education. When she returned in 1990, *Myth and Magic* was already in full swing and she recalls enjoying the challenge of working on a project requiring such a great deal of imagination. At college she specialised in painting as well as drawing, and her colour work can be seen in the illustrations for Allan Frost's The Stracyl of Unity. Amongst Jessica's favourite studies is The Dark Dragon and its big brother, The Dragon of Darkness. She also admires in particular some of Sharon Riley's larger designs, such as The VII Seekers of Knowledge and The Dragon Master.

Current Pieces

THE MOON WIZARD

CODE: 3063
ISSUED: August 1991
DESIGNER: JW MODELLER: AS
SIZE: 2½" x 1¾" x 3½"
ISSUE PRICE: £12.95

Aware that all wizards in the collection so far had worn hats, Jessica Watson decided to give The Moon Wizard a cap instead, to fit in more with the theme of the study. The Moon Wizard also represents the beginning of a new experiment with crystals on the standard-sized studies — he is equipped with an additional red crystal. (Eagle-eyed collectors will have noted, however, that he originally appeared without it in the 1991 *Myth and Magic* catalogue.)

THE DRAGON OF THE STARS

Or 'Dragon of the Star', as it perhaps might be called, so prominent is the dragon's emblem. No variations are known to exist.

CODE: 3064
ISSUED: August 1991
DESIGNER: JW MODELLER: ML
SIZE: 3" x 2 ½" x 3⅛"
ISSUE PRICE: £17.50

THE SORCERESS OF LIGHT

A relative — in looks, at least — of The Siren (3002). A prototype was produced with the Sorceress holding a globe, though the study was never issued in this form.

CODE: 3065
ISSUED: August 1991
DESIGNER: JW MODELLER: ML
SIZE: 2 ½" x 1 ¼" x 3 ¼"
ISSUE PRICE: £12.95

Also, prior to release, her vital statistics were altered to give her a more buxom appearance. SCHEDULED FOR RETIREMENT: 31st December 1994.

THE JEWELLED DRAGON

Jewelled not because its skin is encrusted with jewels, as some think, but because it is surrounded by jewels, and appreciative of them, too.

CODE: 3066
ISSUED: August 1991
DESIGNER: JW MODELLER: AS
SIZE: 3" x 1¾" x 3"
ISSUE PRICE: £12.95

RUNELORE

Just for the record: this study is pronounced 'rune - lore', not 'runnylore' as some claim. The basis is the lore (stories) of the runes (stones), and the study depicts a wizard reading to a dragon.

CODE: 3068
ISSUED: August 1991
DESIGNER: SR MODELLER: RG
SIZE: 3¹/₈" x 1³/₄" x 2³/₄"
ISSUE PRICE: £17.50

THE DRAGON QUEEN

Like The Fairy Queen (3069), a study incorporating both a red bead and a crystal. The dragon's tail has a tendency to bend during production, and its position varies

CODE: 3070
ISSUED: January 1992
DESIGNER: JW MODELLER: AS
SIZE: 2¹/₈" x 2 ⁵/₈" x 3³/₈"
ISSUE PRICE: £18.95

THE ICE DRAGON

In Mould 1 The Ice Dragon's right arm extends prominently outwards, but this caused ripping in the moulds, and so for Mould 2 it was drawn in and more across the body (during Autumn 1993). As a point of interest, this is the dragon Snowscale in Allan Frost's The Stracyl of Unity.

CODE: 3071
ISSUED: January 1992
DESIGNER: JW MODELLER: AS
SIZE: 2 ¹/₄" x 2" x 3"
ISSUE PRICE: £13.95

THE SLEEPY DRAGON

Another innovation for the collection was the use and positioning of the small crystal into the Sleepy Dragon's resting place. It must be considered a success as The Sleepy Dragon is a very popular study — so popular in fact that it was used as a weapon in a disagreement, as reported in The Tudor Mint's local press! Sharon Riley in fact produced a design for this study, but it was reworked by Jessica Watson.

CODE: 3072
ISSUED: January 1992
DESIGNER: JW (after SR) MODELLER: ML
SIZE: 3¹/₄" x 1³/₄" x 2⁵/₈"
ISSUE PRICE: £13.95

THE UNICORN OF LIGHT

CODE: 3073
ISSUED: January 1992
DESIGNER: JW **MODELLER:** AS
SIZE: 2¼" x 1¾" x 3½"
ISSUE PRICE: £13.95

One of the January 1992 releases that designer Jessica Watson wanted to feature a bead as well as a crystal.

STARSPELL

CODE: 3074
ISSUED: January 1992
DESIGNER: JW **MODELLER:** ML
SIZE: 2½" x 2" x 3½"
ISSUE PRICE: £13.95

The first study to feature a blue bead, in the centre of the wizard's star (which you certainly can't avoid noticing!).

CODE: 3075
ISSUED: January 1992
DESIGNER: JW (after SR) **MODELLER:** RG
SIZE: 2 ¾" x 1 ½" x 3 ½"
ISSUE PRICE: £18.95

THE VISIONARY

Sharon Riley initiated the design for this study and Jessica Watson completed it. The inspiration came from The Mirror of Galadriel (5032) in The Lord of the Rings collection. Just one prototype was sent to a member at random (with a Certificate of Authenticity) during Collectors Club renewal time; this version has a larger crystal that the version on general release, which 'fills' the space in the top of the font.

THE CRYSTAL SPELL ▶

CODE: 3076
ISSUED: January 1992
DESIGNER: JW MODELLER: ML
SIZE: $2^{5}/_{8}$" x $1^{5}/_{8}$" x $3^{1}/_{2}$"
ISSUE PRICE: £13.95

The wizard here is depicted casting a spell. One or two features about him (notably the left hand) have resulted in the alternative name 'The Mincing Wizard' (courtesy of those irreverent model makers at The Tudor Mint).

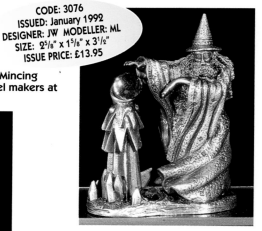

UNICORN RIDER

CODE: 3077
ISSUED: January 1992
DESIGNER: JW MODELLER: AS
SIZE: $3^{1}/_{4}$" x $1^{1}/_{4}$" x 3"
ISSUE PRICE: £13.95

The first 200 of this study were issued with a shorter horn (Mould 1), but it was then changed to a more regular size (Mould 2). Also, the unicorn's feet were altered to give more strength and support. Allan Frost says that Unicorn Rider "could be" Coraniel (an anagram taken from his daughter Caroline's name) in The Stracyl of Unity.

Designer Profile

HELEN COVENTRY

Helen joined W.A.P. Watson Ltd. in 1991, and has worked on designs for jewellery, display stands and packaging (including the new *Myth and Magic* box design for 1995). Her first *Myth and Magic* figurine was The Rising of the Phoenix and since then she has designed The Wizard of the Skies and most of the 'Demon' studies from *Dark Secrets*. She is looking forward to being more involved with *Myth and Magic* in the future, and is constantly thinking of new ideas. Despite being involved in creating original artwork these days, Helen actually specialised in photography for her degree in Design at North Staffordshire Polytechnic.

CODE: 3078
ISSUED: August 1992
DESIGNER: SR MODELLER: AS
SIZE: 2" x 2" x $3^{1}/_{2}$"
ISSUE PRICE: £13.95

THE LOREMAKER

Sharon Riley particularly enjoyed designing this study, with its theme of relaxation in the woods. In the first production run (Mould 1), it was issued with the wrong number on the base plate (3085); but this was soon corrected (Mould 2).

CODE: 3079
ISSUED: August 1992
DESIGNER: SR/M MODELLER: AS
SIZE: 2 1/8" x 2 1/4" x 3 1/2"
ISSUE PRICE: £18.95

THE DRAGON'S ENCHANTRESS

This study was inspired by a design created by a *Myth and Magic* collector, John Sparrow, which Sharon Riley then reworked. John was the winner of a 'Design a Study' competition featured in the Methtintdour Times (issue 4); his original title was 'The Dragon Queen', but this had already been used for study number 3070. SCHEDULED FOR RETIREMENT: 31st December 1994.

CODE: 3080
ISSUED: August 1992
DESIGNER: JW/M MODELLER: RG
SIZE: 2 5/8" x 2" x 2 3/4"
ISSUE PRICE: £13.95

THE LEAF SPIRIT ▶

The 'Design a Study' competition in the Methtintdour Times also generated this piece. Julia Almeida came third in the competition and Jessica Watson redrew her design, with some slight alterations, to produce The Leaf Spirit. SCHEDULED FOR RETIREMENT: 31st December 1994.

THE WIZARD OF THE FUTURE

In Mould 1 the wizard's cloak is thinner; it was soon thickened up for Mould 2. The subject himself does look futuristic, and Sharon Riley says she was glad of the chance to draw a wizard who wasn't quite so 'old-fashioned'.

CODE: 3081
ISSUED: August 1992
DESIGNER: SR MODELLER: RG
SIZE: 3" x 1 3/4" x 4"
ISSUE PRICE: £13.95

THE SWAMP DRAGON

CODE: 3082
ISSUED: August 1992
DESIGNER: SR MODELLER: AS
SIZE: 3" x 2" x 3 1/2"
ISSUE PRICE: £13.95

A popular study. The original design was slightly higher than the finished model, but nevertheless the end result has a great deal of movement.

THE DRAGON OF THE ▶ SKULLS

Jessica Watson is particularly fond of this dragon — one of her own designs — "apart from the left foot," she says. Well, nobody's perfect.

CODE: 3083
ISSUED: August 1992
DESIGNER: JW MODELLER: RG
SIZE: 2¼" x 1½" x 3½"
ISSUE PRICE: £13.95

CODE: 3084
ISSUED: August 1992
DESIGNER: JW MODELLER: AS
SIZE: 3" x 2" x 3½"
ISSUE PRICE: £13.95

◀ THE DARK DRAGON

The Dark Dragon was later remodelled and enlarged to become The Dragon of Darkness (No.3322). Jessica Watson certainly succeeded in her brief to produce a fierce dragon, and the larger version reflects this even more so. In Mould 1 the back of the dragon's left leg is unfilled, but as it tended to break off, it was filled in for Mould 2.

THE DRAGON OF LIGHT ▼

Although this study is attributed to Roger Gibbons on the name plate, he only made the glowing star; Anthony Slocombe sculpted the rest.

CODE: 3085
ISSUED: August 1992
DESIGNER: JW MODELLER: RG/AS
SIZE: 2¾" x 2" x 3⅜"
ISSUE PRICE: £13.95

THE FOUNTAIN OF LIFE

CODE: 3092
ISSUED: January 1993
DESIGNER: JW MODELLER: AS
SIZE: 2½" x 1¾" x 3¼"
ISSUE PRICE: £14.75

A study of a wizard in harmony with his world, surrounded by many natural features.

THE DAWN OF THE DRAGON

CODE: 3093
ISSUED: January 1993
DESIGNER: JW MODELLER: RG (ML)
SIZE: 2³/₈" x 1³/₄" x 3¹/₄"
ISSUE PRICE: £14.75

When shown at a trade show in February 1993, reaction to the original version was that the double-headed dragon appeared somewhat lifeless. So a month into production, the study was remodelled; the dragon's heads were set at different angles (Mould 2), instead of 'flat', to give the piece greater movement and a more dramatic effect. At the same time the wings were also altered. Approximately 400 Mould 1's were released prior to the change. Should this study have been called The Protector of the Young? See 3097.

THE DRAGON OF PREHISTORY

CODE: 3094
ISSUED: January 1993
DESIGNER: JW MODELLER: RG
SIZE: 2¹/₂" x 1³/₄" x 3"
ISSUE PRICE: £14.75

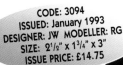

The Dragon of Prehistory certainly lives up to his name, looking suitably 'prehistoric' and surrounded by all manner of fossils and other remnants of his age. This is one of Jessica Watson's favourite studies.

THE DEFENDER OF THE CRYSTAL

Pegasus is seen warding off those who would attempt to steal the crystal.

CODE: 3095
ISSUED: January 1993
DESIGNER: JW MODELLER: AS
SIZE: 3" x 1¹/₂" x 3"
ISSUE PRICE: £14.75

Model Maker Profile

ROGER GIBBONS
(Chief Model Maker)

Born in 1954, Roger Gibbons started his career as a precious stone salesman in Birmingham's Jewellery Quarter before gaining an apprenticeship in W.A.P. Watson Ltd.'s Model Making Department; part of his training involved a three year jewellery course at Mid-Warwickshire College of Higher Education under Rex Billingham. Since then he has worked on fashion jewellery, souvenirs, giftware (including the *Mirella* range), *Crystalflame* and the Victorian scenes that launched The Tudor Mint name. Roger modelled the first *Myth and Magic* figurines from Sharon Riley's designs and has worked on a great number since (as the frequency of his name on base plates testifies). However, as Chief Model Maker he also has administrative duties to consider and doesn't sculpt quite as much as he has done in the past. In 1994 he celebrates 20 years with the company.

Current Pieces

THE RISING OF THE PHOENIX

CODE: 3096
ISSUED: January 1993
DESIGNER: HC MODELLER: ML
SIZE: 2³/₄" x 1³/₄" x 2³/₄"
ISSUE PRICE: £14.75

Helen Coventry had worked on other facets of the collection (such as the paper knives) but this was her first design for a *Myth and Magic* study proper. It was also the first appearance in the collection of the Phoenix, the legendary Arabian bird said to set fire to itself and rise anew from the ashes every 500 years.

THE PROTECTOR OF THE YOUNG

CODE: 3097
ISSUED: January 1993
DESIGNER: JW MODELLER: ML (RG)
SIZE: 2³/₈" x 1³/₄" x 3¹/₄"
ISSUE PRICE: £14.75

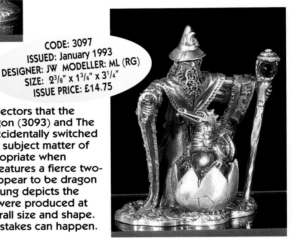

Suspicions abound amongst collectors that the names of The Dawn of the Dragon (3093) and The Protector of the Young were accidentally switched round prior to release. Certainly the subject matter of these two studies seems more appropriate when reversed: The Dawn of the Dragon features a fierce two-headed beast standing over what appear to be dragon eggs, whilst The Protector of the Young depicts the birth of a new dragon. The studies were produced at the same time and are similar in overall size and shape. Name plates get muddled up . . . mistakes can happen. We rest our case.

CODE: 3098
ISSUED: January 1993
DESIGNER: JW MODELLER: AS
SIZE: 3¹/₂" x 1¹/₂" x 3¹/₂"
ISSUE PRICE: £14.75

THE UNICORNS OF FREEDOM

It may have taken three years before they did it, but here the Spirits of the Forest (3051) finally prove they *can* run.

THE KEEPER OF THE SKULLS

CODE: 3099
ISSUED: January 1993
DESIGNER: JW MODELLER: RG
SIZE: 2" x 2" x 3¼"
ISSUE PRICE: £19.75

I t's the morning after the night
before on a grey winter's day in late 1992. A bleary-
eyed, unshaven face stares blankly back from the
unkind bathroom mirror; its owner runs his hand across
the back of his throbbing head until fingers can be
seen protruding from above his hair. The image freeze-
frames in his mind . . . undoubtedly the most gruesome
sight he has seen in a long while! Soon he is briefing
his designer: "I want a skull sitting in the palm of a
hand." Thus came the unlikely (but true) inspiration for
the most popular piece in the *Myth and Magic* range —
in its first year alone 25,000 models were sold. Such
obvious appeal hinted to The Tudor Mint that there
may be a market for a more macabre range, and as a
direct result, *Dark Secrets* were born.

THE WIZARD OF THE SERPENTS

W hen asked to explain this study, Sharon
Riley replied: "It's The Wizard of the
Serpents." So there you are then.

CODE: 3100
ISSUED: August 1993
DESIGNER: SR MODELLER: ML
SIZE: 3" x 1⅝" x 3¼"
ISSUE PRICE: £14.75

THE LOVING DRAGONS

I n Mould 1 the dragon's right wing does not
quite touch the base; consequently it tended to break off and was soon remodelled
slightly lower (Mould 2).

CODE: 3101
ISSUED: August 1993
DESIGNER: SR MODELLER: ML
SIZE: 2¼" x 2¾" x 3½"
ISSUE PRICE: £14.75

Current Pieces

THE SWORD MASTER

The Sword Master is seen here celebrating a win in battle. Although the name plate acknowledges Mark Locker as the sculptor of this study, it is in fact the work of Anthony Slocombe.

CODE: 3102
ISSUED: August 1993
DESIGNER: SR MODELLER: ML (AS)
SIZE: 2¹/₂" x 2 ¹/₄" x 3¹/₂"
ISSUE PRICE: £14.75

THE DRAGON OF MYSTERY

In Mould 1 the dragon's right arm is quite thin and it used to snap off. It was thickened for added strength in Mould 2. However, this did not quite do the trick and so a Mould 3 was created in January 1994 with the dragon's wings extended higher for more support.

CODE: 3103
ISSUED: August 1993
DESIGNER: SR MODELLER: ML
SIZE: 2¹/₂" x 2 ¹/₄" x 3¹/₈"
ISSUE PRICE: £14.75

THE WIZARD OF THE SKIES ▼

Although officially called The Wizard of the Skies, the word 'The' is missing from the name plate. On this study, the wizard's staff, which features a kestrel's head, was thinner in Mould 1 and broke quite easily; so more feathers were added to overhang the wizard's hand (Mould 2). For some curious reason which he himself is unable to explain, Mark Locker decided to inscribe on the wizard's hat the Dalek name for Dr. Who.

CODE: 3104
ISSUED: January 1994
DESIGNER: HC MODELLER: ML
SIZE: 2¹/₂" x 1 ³/₄" x 3¹/₂"
ISSUE PRICE: £14.95

CODE: 3105
ISSUED: January 1994
DESIGNER: JW MODELLER: AS
SIZE: 2³/₄" x 2 ³/₄" x 3¹/₈"
ISSUE PRICE: £14.95

THE DRAGON OF THE TREASURE

A greedy, stealing dragon. Together with The Wizard of the Skies (3104) this piece was prereleased by several months in Canada, for a mail order catalogue company.

THE WIZARD OF THE LAKE

CODE: 3106
ISSUED: January 1994
DESIGNER: SR MODELLER: RG
SIZE: 3¼" x 2" x 3½"
ISSUE PRICE: £14.95

A study inspired by Charon who, in Greek mythology, was the hideous old man who ferried the spirits of the dead over the rivers Styx and Acheron (for which he would charge the fare of an obulus).

BANISHING THE DRAGON

This was model maker Steve Darnley's first contribution to *Myth and Magic*, and he was pleased with the result. In particular he was satisfied that it was possible to cast the wizard with a pointing finger; such delicate detail would normally be problematic, and probably be altered. Happily not in this instance. The nameplate, incidentally, has an 'of' — Banishing of the Dragon.

CODE: 3107
ISSUED: January 1994
DESIGNER: SR MODELLER: SD
SIZE: 2⅝" x 1 ⅝" x 3⅞"
ISSUE PRICE: £14.95

▼ THE DRAGON'S CASTLE

An almost Art-Deco style castle, the study was released initially with a hollowed interior (Mould 1), but after a few months of production it became a solid piece and was cast as one to avoid soldering time (Mould 2). In the process it became heavier.

CODE: 3108
ISSUED: January 1994
DESIGNER: JW MODELLER: RG
SIZE: 2 ½" x 1 ½" x 3 ½"
ISSUE PRICE: £14.95

THE MYSTICAL TRAVELLER ▶

In Jessica Watson's original design Pegasus was being led by the young boy; but this proved impractical in production and he sits astride him in the released model.

CODE: 3109
ISSUED: January 1994
DESIGNER: JW MODELLER: ML
SIZE: 3⅛" x 1¼" x 3¼"
ISSUE PRICE: £14.95

Current Pieces

THE ARMOURED DRAGON

CODE: 3110
ISSUED: January 1994
DESIGNER: JW MODELLER: SD
SIZE: 1³/₄" x 2³/₄" x 3¹/₄"
ISSUE PRICE: £14.95

The Armoured Dragon may have survived the 'Drop Test' (see 'How *Myth and Magic* are Made' in Section One) but in its Mould 1 version it was certainly troublesome in transit to the stockists — the back left wing kept falling off. Only 400 or so Mould 1 dragons exist. A hasty remodelling took place; the wings had originally been modelled virtually parallel, so the back wing was repositioned to point downwards and away from the body, thus giving extra strength (Mould 2). However, the new shape gave a problem in casting, and another remodelling took place in March 1994 so that a chain was added for support (Mould 3).

THE HATCHLINGS ▼

Graham Hughes decided that after all the recent "nasty" pieces (especially *Dark Secrets* a return to something cute was required, and The Hatchlings resulted. In the first 200 or so models, the dragon on the left's wings do not touch the egg (Mould 1). They were prone to breakage and were subsequently lowered early on into production (Mould 2).

CODE: 3111
ISSUED: January 1994
DESIGNER: JW MODELLER: SD
SIZE: 2⁷/₈" x 2" x 2¹/₂"
ISSUE PRICE: £14.95

THE DRAGON OF THE ICE CRYSTALS ▼

CODE: 3112
ISSUED: July 1994
DESIGNER: SR MODELLER: AS
SIZE: 2¹/₂" x 1¹/₂" x 3³/₄"
ISSUE PRICE: £17.95

This is the first study to incorporate the new range of crystal shapes and colours.

38

THE MISCHIEVOUS DRAGON

CODE: 3113
ISSUED: July 1994
DESIGNER: SR MODELLER: SD
SIZE: 3" x 2¹/₂" x 3¹/₂"
ISSUE PRICE: £14.95

Study No. 3113 was originally called The Enchanted Glade, and a prototype exists at The Tudor Mint with this on the baseplate. The name was changed to The Mischievous Dragon to reflect more accurately the content of Sharon Riley's design — i.e. the dragon stealing the crystal from the sleeping wizard.

CODE: 3114
ISSUED: July 1994
DESIGNER: SR MODELLER: SD
SIZE: 2⁷/₈" x 2" x 2¹/₂"
ISSUE PRICE: £17.95

THE CRYSTAL UNICORN

This is Steve Darnley's first 'unicorn' study, based on Sharon Riley's design. (Incidentally, Steve has two children — Leanne (7) and Ben (5) — and he takes pride in pointing out to them his models for sale in shop windows.)

CODE: 3115
ISSUED: July 1994
DESIGNER: SR MODELLER: ML
SIZE: 2" x 3" x 3 ¹/₂"
ISSUE PRICE: £17.95

THE SUMMONER OF LIGHT

An impressive example of how the use of a large crystal makes it an integral part of the design, rather than a subsidiary element.

THE MAJESTIC DRAGON

CODE: 3116
ISSUED: July 1994
DESIGNER: SR MODELLER: AS
SIZE: 3" x 2" x 3"
ISSUE PRICE: £17.95

A maternal dragon, with sleeping dragonets wrapped up in her tail.

CODE: 3117
ISSUED: July 1994
DESIGNER: SR MODELLER: RG
SIZE: 2 ½" x 2 ¾" x 3 ¼"
ISSUE PRICE: £14.95

THE PROUD PEGASUS

What might otherwise have been a relatively conventional *Myth and Magic* study is given a new dimension by the larger crystal, which Pegasus appears to have stumbled across.

Model Maker Profile

MARK LOCKER
(Model Maker)

Model making has always interested Mark Locker, ever since his grandfather taught him to carve wood as a boy. Thus, as one of W.A.P. Watson's two solderers nine years ago (now there are twelve!), he used to pester Roger Gibbons in his spare time to teach him the finer skills of his craft. Eventually Roger said, "Come and find out for yourself" — and Mark was thrown in at the deep end as a full-time model maker. This was just prior to the genesis of *Myth and Magic,* and he worked on the Tudor Mint Victorian scenes before becoming 'Mister *Fantasy and Legend*' to Roger's 'Mister *Myth and Magic.*' But *Fantasy and Legend* did not work out so well, and Mark has since sculpted a considerable number of *Myth and Magic* studies as well as turning his hand to other requirements. His favourite study is The Tortured Skull (*Dark Secrets*) as he took great pains to get the anatomy just right, and he also admires Anthony Slocombe's work on The Dragon of Darkness.

THE DRAGON MASTER
(Limited Edition)

CODE: 3300
ISSUED: January 1990
EDITION SIZE: 7,500
DESIGNER: SR MODELLER: RG
SIZE: 8" x 8" x 9"
ISSUE PRICE: £175

Although the largest study produced up to that date, Sharon Riley's original design for The Dragon Master was even larger; it had to be toned down as the piece would have been simply too heavy. This was also the first *Myth and Magic* limited edition study, restricted to 7,500. As at summer 1991, 2,963 had been sold, and a year later the figure had risen to 3,287. However, the piece was not originally issued as a limited edition; the decision was made towards the end of the first year of production (1990).

Model Maker Profile

ANTHONY SLOCOMBE
(Model Maker)

Like Roger Gibbons, Anthony Slocombe studied under Rex Billingham at Mid-Warwickshire College of Further Education. After an initial three year stint with W.A.P. Watson Ltd., he left the company, only to return again four years later. During his time away he worked for Citadel Miniatures, sculpting fantasy figures, which stood him in good stead when he later found himself immersed in creating *Myth and Magic* back at The Tudor Mint; his first model was Le Morte d'Arthur. He likes to give his pieces a hard edge to them, especially the dragons, and The Dragon of Darkness is a favourite of his — "nice and mean and nasty." His son Jack (aged 7) has been immortalised on more than one study: his initials (JOS) can be seen on The Well of Aspirations and the name 'Jack' appears on The Chamber of the Skulls. Anthony was born in Hall Green, Birmingham, in 1962 and having moved all round Britain since, now finds himself back in Hall Green!

CODE: 3301
ISSUED: January 1990
DESIGNER: SR MODELLER: RG
SIZE: 3⁷/₈" x 1⁵/₈" x 3"
ISSUE PRICE: £17.95

THE MAGICAL ENCOUNTER

Graham Hughes intended this as the centre piece for collections, with a neat bit of self-advertising on the banner. This is the smallest of the larger series and the only one not to have a plinth base (perhaps some day a plinth will come!). In Mould 1 the tail of the dragon on the right slants inwards; Mould 2 has the tail slanting outwards. The U.S. version highlights the name 'Fantasy Creations'; this was amended in June 1994 to read 'Tudor Mint Inc.' to reflect the change of distributor.

THE KEEPER OF THE MAGIC

Originally the first two larger studies (this and 3303) were numbered as part of the standard-sized collection as they were not envisaged as 'larger' at the time. Indeed Sharon Riley's designs were of standard size and only during modelmaking was the scale increased. Shortly afterwards the decision was made to begin a new number series, and this study and Summoning the Elements were both given a wooden plinth and reissued as 3302 and 3303 respectively. Mould 1 had a single large, clear crystal; several other colours followed, including blue (the most common). For Mould 2, the mount of the study was redesigned to accommodate two crystals: at first one was clear and one blue; now both are blue.

The Keeper of the Magic

CODE: 3302
(originally 3025)
ISSUED: January 1990
DESIGNER: SR MODELLER: RG
SIZE: 4" x 2 ¹/₂" x 3¹/₂"
ISSUE PRICE: £34.95

Current Pieces

MEETING OF THE UNICORNS

According to Sharon Riley, this study was inspired by the work of artist Peter E. Pracownik. Although attributed to Roger Gibbons, it was sculpted by Mark Locker. Originally issued with cubic crystals.

CODE: 3306
ISSUED: January 1990
DESIGNER: SR MODELLER: RG (ML)
SIZE: 5" x 2½" x 4"
ISSUE PRICE: £34.95

The Meeting of The Unicorns

CODE: 3308
ISSUED: August 1990
EDITION SIZE: 7,500
DESIGNER: SR MODELLER: ML
SIZE: 7½" x 7½" x 8½"
ISSUE PRICE: £175

The VII Seekers of Knowledge

THE VII SEEKERS OF KNOWLEDGE
(Limited Edition)

The second very large limited edition study. By the summer of 1991, 1,889 had been sold and a year later the figure had risen to 2,392. The study depicts seven wizards come to pay homage and to learn from the Master Dragon. The Mould 1 dragon had a tendency to lose a wing or two, so in Mould 2 his shoulders were filled in adjacent to his body.

LE MORTE D'ARTHUR

CODE: 3309
ISSUED: August 1990
DESIGNER: SR MODELLER: AS
SIZE: 4¹/₂" x 3¹/₂" x 3¹/₂"
ISSUE PRICE: £49.95

A study based not only on Mallory's great medieval work of the same name printed in 1485, but also on John Boorman's great contemporary film 'Excalibur'. Some artistic license has been applied, as the study depicts Guinevere kneeling as Arthur's body lies on his tomb. In both book and film his body is borne away over the water to Avalon. In Mould 1 the pillars were nearer to the edge of the base, and the baseplate credits Mark Locker, when in fact it was modelled by Anthony Slocombe (his first *Myth and Magic* study). About 800 models were released before the baseplate was corrected, the pillars were moved nearer to the tomb, and the gap between Arthur's crown and the nearest pillar was filled in (Mould 2). Within the portals of The Tudor Mint an alternative scenario for this study exists ... but the less said about that the better!

THE MAGICAL VISION

CODE: 3310
ISSUED: August 1990
DESIGNER: SR MODELLER: RG (AS)
SIZE: 4¹/₂" x 3¹/₂" x 4¹/₄"
ISSUE PRICE: £49.95

S haron Riley's spectacular original design showed the wizard actually casting a spell, with stars and magic emanating from his hand and surrounding the whole piece. Unfortunately this could not be translated into a production model and the design had to be toned down. In Mould 1 the wizard's right arm is raised straight upwards, the columns are nearer to the corners and are more matching, and the staff is thinner. In Mould 2 the arm slopes forward, the columns are moved inwards and the staff is thicker.

Current Pieces

THE ALTAR OF ENLIGHTENMENT

A study with a sacrifical theme. In Mould 1 the wizard at the back was further away from the altar, but this was changed to make the study more realistic. The setting for the crystal was also altered for Mould 2, to allow for a slightly larger stone. The Altar itself was originally designed for a huge 'Stonehenge' study which never came to fruition.

CODE: 3312
ISSUED: January 1991
DESIGNER: SR MODELLER: ML
SIZE: 5" x 3½" x 4"
ISSUE PRICE: £49.95

The Altar of Enlightenment

THE POWER OF THE CRYSTAL
(Limited Edition)

T here was much collaboration between designer and sculptor on this huge study, and until it really started to take shape Jessica Watson described the first stages as "a bit of a heap". It took Anthony Slocombe a whole month to complete the sculpting, with many alterations along the way. Both agree, however, that the finished study was well worthwhile. The low edition size reflects the high price of the largest, heaviest and most expensive *Myth and Magic* study to date. In six months The Tudor Mint had received 348 orders and a year later (summer 1992) the number had risen to 849. Each study has the edition number stamped into the metal, and when four figures were reached a new plate was required at The Tudor Mint. Unfortunately the plate read 4,000 instead of 1,000 and the mistake was not noticed until 15 studies had been despatched; so 1001 to 1015 actually read 4001 to 4015. Some have been traced and corrected, but there are still others out there with incorrect numbers. In addition, the first five studies were released with pewter eyes instead of the usual red crystals.

CODE: 3313
ISSUED: January 1991
EDITION SIZE: 3,500
DESIGNER: JW MODELLER: AS
SIZE: 11" x 11" x 9"
ISSUE PRICE: £350

The Power of the Crystal

THE AWAKENING

CODE: 3314
ISSUED: January 1992
DESIGNER: JP MODELLER: JP
SIZE: 4¹/₂" x 3¹/₂" x 3¹/₂"
ISSUE PRICE: £37.95

This is the only larger study not designed and modelled within the company. John Pickering is a freelance designer/modelmaker who presented The Tudor Mint with an example of his work — this very piece. Graham Hughes liked it, and in January 1992 The Awakening became part of the collection. The difference in style is fairly apparent, due partly to John's personal technique and also the fact that he is used to sculpting models to be cast in resin, not white metal. He also designed the Fantasy Chess Set (4305), the boxes for The Lord of the Rings Collection, and the Crystal Keepers.

The Awakening

THE CRYSTAL DRAGON

One of the Tudor Mint's mail order catalogue customers made a specific request for a study with 'a big dragon and a big crystal' — and that's precisely what they got!

CODE: 3315
ISSUED: August 1992
DESIGNER: JW MODELLER: AS
SIZE: 4¹/₂" x 3" x 6"
ISSUE PRICE: £59.95

The Crystal Dragon

Model Maker Profile

STEVE DARNLEY

(Model Maker)

Steve Darnley was born in 1962. He worked for W.A.P. Watson Ltd. for three years (in Casting and Mould Making), then left for nearly five years before returning as a model maker in 1991. Although always interested in model making, he has never had any formal training and joined the department purely on the merits of his self-taught skills gained using tools hand made for him by his father. As the 'new boy' he tended to work initially on souvenirs but is much more involved with *Myth and Magic* these days. His first study was Banishing the Dragon and he also sculpted The Armoured Dragon (a favourite of his), The Hatchlings and a number of *Dark Secrets* studies. He prides himself on trying to make the 'backs' of his studies as interesting as the 'fronts', this being the part not covered by the original design drawings and which allows for greater creativity.

THE GATHERING OF THE UNICORNS

CODE: 3318
ISSUED: August 1992
EDITION SIZE: 5,000
DESIGNER: JW MODELLER: AS/RG
SIZE: 7¼" x 7¼" x 7½"
ISSUE PRICE: £185

Perhaps more accurately referred to as 'The Parting of the Unicorns', as in Mould 1 they frequently parted company with the base! This was because there were no supports for the unicorns, but over the years logs and branches have been added to create a Mould 2 version. Jessica Watson originally envisaged a maiden rather than a wizard, but it was felt that a wizard was more in keeping with the collection. The wizard in question was actually intended for the never-released 'Stonehenge'. The Gathering of the Unicorns was modelled jointly by Roger Gibbons and Anthony Slocombe.

THE INVOCATION

Another sacrificial study which benefited from the unreleased 'Stonehenge' study. This time it was the rocks that were 'purloined'. In Mould 1 the right arm of the wizard at the back had no bangle; it was added for strength in Mould 2, which also featured a change of crystal.

CODE: 3319
ISSUED: August 1993
DESIGNER: SR MODELLER: ML
SIZE: 5" x 3¾" x 4¼"
ISSUE PRICE: £49.95

Current Pieces

THE FIGHTING DRAGONS

Rather a one-sided fight, in fact, as one of the dragons is without arms!

CODE: 3320
ISSUED: August 1993
DESIGNER: JW MODELLER: AS
SIZE: 5¼" x 3½" x 3½"
ISSUE PRICE: £39.95

The Fighting Dragons

CODE: 3321
ISSUED: August 1993
DESIGNER: SR MODELLER: ML
SIZE: 4½" x 3" x 3"
ISSUE PRICE: £33.50

The Playful Dolphins

THE PLAYFUL DOLPHINS

A study released to replace The Dance of the Dolphins, which had not proved popular with collectors.

THE DRAGON OF DARKNESS

CODE: 3322
ISSUED: January 1994
DESIGNER: AS (after JW) MODELLER: AS
SIZE: 5" x 3½" x 5¼"
ISSUE PRICE: £39.95

The Dragon of Darkness is the first larger study to be inspired directly by a standard-sized study, The Dark Dragon. Mould 1 had no mount for the stone, and only about 800 exist. Mould 2 added the mount, and in May 1994 Mould 3 was issued with the addition of an extra branch on the tree as a support for the dragon's left wing, similar to the one supporting the right wing (resulting in comments that it should be re-christened 'The Crucified Dragon'). Anthony Slocombe sculpted this study without design drawings, using The Dark Dragon as his direct source, the original design for which was created by Jessica Watson.

THE DESTROYER OF THE CRYSTAL

CODE: 3323
ISSUED: July 1994
DESIGNER: SR MODELLER: SD
SIZE: 5¼" x 3¾" x 4¼"
ISSUE PRICE: £49.95

The wizard with the sword at full stretch, combined with the idea of setting the crystal horizontally, gives this study great power. Again, the crystal shape gave rise to the overall theme.

Current Pieces

A TRANQUIL MOMENT

CODE: 3324
ISSUED: July 1994
DESIGNER: SR MODELLER: ML
SIZE: 5" x 3" x 4"
ISSUE PRICE: £49.95

N ot so much 'tranquil' as 'momentous', with Pegasus, the unicorn and the wizard at last appearing on a study together. But of course The Tudor Mint know best when naming their studies; after all, how many collectors would feel comfortable walking into a shop and asking for "A Momentous Moment, please!"

CODE: 3325
ISSUED: July 1994
DESIGNER: SR MODELLER: RG
ISSUE PRICE: £59.95

THE GREAT EARTH DRAGON

A tour-de-force for crystal lovers, with spectacular coloured wings as well as a freestanding crystal. Graham Hughes knew exactly what he wanted in this study and worked along side Sharon Riley during the design stage.

The Great Earth Dragon

Current Pieces

Myth and Magic
Retired Studies

Listed here are the studies in the main collection which have been retired (i.e. discontinued) by The Tudor Mint at some stage, up to and including December 1993, and as no further retirements have been announced prior to December 1994 (apart from Collectors Club and Limited Availability studies, which are itemised elsewhere), the list will remain accurate until then. Pieces scheduled for retirement are highlighted as such in the previous section. Secondary market values of these studies can be found beginning on page 132.

Typical *Myth and Magic* base marking: THE WINGED SERPENT by Roger Gibbons 3007 WAPW © U.K. (For details of variations, see Collecting Myth and Magic in Section One.)

STANDARD SIZE

THE EVIL OF GREED

Picture the scene. You're searching for that perfect birthday present. Your eyes alight upon a crystal-bearing wizard, standing guard over a hoard of treasure — excellent! Then you pick it up and find it's called 'The Evil of Greed' . . . perhaps not the ideal present after all! Needless to say, this study proved unpopular and was soon retired. It was later remodelled and released as The Keeper of the Treasure. Ironically, Sharon Riley did not intend the study to be 'evil' at all; she considered the wizard to be wondering at the beauty of the crystal! But then if the theme had been adhered to and the piece called 'The Wonderous Treaure', there would have been no eagerly sought-after Evil of Greed's!

CODE: 3003
ISSUED: March 1989
RETIRED: December 1989
DESIGNER: SR MODELLER: RG
SIZE: 1½" x 1¾" x 3½"
ISSUE PRICE: £9.95

THE ENCHANTED CASTLE

The first of several castles in the collection, The Enchanted Castle was originally issued without an extra wall between the two turrets (Mould 1). One was added soon after the first production run, to give the piece extra strength (Mould 2). This second version is a lot easier to find than the first.

CODE: 3005
ISSUED: March 1989
RETIRED: June 1991
DESIGNER: SR MODELLER: RG
SIZE: 1 ¼" x 1 ¼" x 3 ½"
ISSUE PRICE: £9.95

THE WINGED SERPENT

The piece was originally issued with both wings raised high, in a V-shape (Mould 1), but these tended to snap off and solderers were asked to solder the wings on parallel. However, breakages still occurred, so support was given to the neck, and the wings were remodelled to sit lower, with the left wing attached to the serpent's tail (Mould 2). Differences occur in the positioning and length of the tail, but these are production variants, not mould alterations.

CODE: 3007
ISSUED: March 1989
RETIRED: June 1991
DESIGNER: SR MODELLER: RG
SIZE: 1½" x 1¼" x 3½"
ISSUE PRICE: £9.95

THE WHITE WITCH

Only about 400 models exist with the 'hands apart' (Mould 1): they tended to break off and were soon remodelled to touch over the crystal (Mould 2). Differences in the positions of the hands over the crystal are soldering (production) variations only. The nameplate says Roger Gibbons, but The White Witch was modelled by Mark Locker.

CODE: 3008
ISSUED: March 1989
RETIRED: December 1991
DESIGNER: SR MODELLER: RG (ML)
SIZE: 2" x 1½" x 3½"
ISSUE PRICE: £9.95

THE MASTER WIZARD ▼

CODE: 3009
ISSUED: March 1989
RETIRED: December 1993
DESIGNER: SR MODELLER: RG
SIZE: 1½" x 1¾" x 3¼"
ISSUE PRICE: £9.95

Five of the original twelve studies were wizards, and The Master Wizard survived in the collection until December 1993. Two versions exist. In Mould 1, the apex of the wizard's throne does not join at the top, and the wizard's sleeve is shorter; later the top of the throne became a full circle, and strength was added to the right arm by thickening his cloak sleeve.

CODE: 3010
ISSUED: March 1989
RETIRED: December 1989
DESIGNER: SR MODELLER: RG
SIZE: 1½" x 1¼" x 2¼"
ISSUE PRICE: £9.95

THE INFERNAL DEMON

An infernal nuisance for many collectors . . . so difficult to obtain as it is! This was one of the first batch of retirements, and is especially hard to obtain in the original 'arm up' version (where the right arm is raised). Three 'moulds' exist: the arm-up, long-horned version (Mould 1); the arm-up, short-horned version (Mould 2); and the arm-down version (Mould 3).

The arm was lowered to avoid breakage in transit, and the horns were shortened due to production problems (they tended to rip the moulds during extraction). So sought after is the 'arm up' Infernal Demon that The Tudor Mint had to appeal through The Methtintdour Times for a replacement when their copy 'disappeared'. Needless to say, they received very few replies!

THE WARRIOR KNIGHT

About 800 Warrior Knights exist with the knight's right arm angled towards his head so that the sword extends past his head (Mould 1), but this was changed so that the arm is held at 90 degrees and the sword end is touching the knight's helmet. The study was soon discontinued as it was felt that it did not fit in with the rest of the collection.

CODE: 3011
ISSUED: March 1989
RETIRED: December 1990
DESIGNER: SR MODELLER: RG
SIZE: 3" X 1" X 3 ¼"
ISSUE PRICE: £9.95

THE DEADLY COMBAT ▼

The Deadly Combat appeared in three versions in its brief, nine-month life. Originally the dragon's wings were less 'fleshy' (Mould 1), but they were soon filled in (Mould 2). The base was then reduced in size and the wings were brought slightly together (Mould 3) for the simple reason that the study was too big for its box! This restyling had no affect on collectors, however, who argued that that if the combat were deadly, it was likely that it would be the dragon who died! The study was later restyled again and reissued as George and the Dragon.

CODE: 3012
ISSUED: March 1989
RETIRED: December 1989
DESIGNER: SR MODELLER: RG
SIZE: 2 ¼" x 2 ¼" x 2 ¾"
ISSUE PRICE: £9.95

Mould 1   Mould 2   Mould 3

Retired Studies

THE OLD HAG

CODE: 3013
ISSUED: May 1989
RETIRED: December 1990
DESIGNER: SR MODELLER: RG
SIZE: 1 ½" x 1 ½" x 3 ½"
ISSUE PRICE: £9.95

Figurines with red beads instead of crystals have achieved a status all of their own in the few years since their brief appearance — between May and July 1989. They were an experiment by The Tudor Mint that collectors originally didn't like, and so beads were removed and crystals put in their place. (Nevertheless, the ideas behind them made sense; in the Old Hag's case she is shining a red lantern, and the effect is somewhat lost in the crystal version.) Even with a crystal (Mould 2), The Old Hag has become a very sought-after piece, but with a red bead (Mould 1), extraordinarily so.

THE CRYSTAL QUEEN

CODE: 3014
ISSUED: May 1989
RETIRED: December 1993
DESIGNER: SR MODELLER: RG
SIZE: 1 ½" x 1 ½" x 4"
ISSUE PRICE: £9.95

Sharon Riley's original design for The Crystal Queen showed both arms outstretched, but during modelling (and before any models were released) the left arm was lowered to her side. The Queen's cloak is composed of diamond-shaped 'crystals' and very early pieces do not have a 'crystal' immediately under her hand (Mould 1); this was added for greater strength (Mould 2).

Mould 2   Mould 1

Mould 1

CODE: 3015
ISSUED: May 1989
RETIRED: December 1990
DESIGNER: SR MODELLER: RG (ML)
SIZE: 1 ¾" x 1 ¾" x 3 ¼"
ISSUE PRICE: £9.95

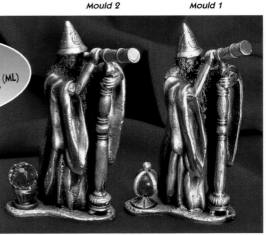

THE ASTRONOMER

Originally The Astronomer had a red bead at his feet (Mould 1) to represent a globe. The change to a crystal (Mould 2) was made two months into production. (Another 'Mark Locker' study issued as a 'Roger Gibbons'.)

Retired Studies

PIPES OF PAN

O ne of several figures in the collection inspired by Greek mythology. Pan is the god of pastures, fields, flocks and forests and is represented as half-man, half-goat. He gained his pipes when the nymph Syrinx tried to flee from his advances — and was turned into the pipes for her pains! Generally the *Myth and Magic* figurines inspired by Greek mythology have not proved popular with collectors, hence their sparse numbers.

CODE: 3016
ISSUED: May 1989
RETIRED: December 1990
DESIGNER: SR MODELLER: RG
SIZE: 1 ¹/₂" x 1 ¹/₄" x 3"
ISSUE PRICE: £9.95

CODE: 3017
ISSUED: May 1989
RETIRED: December 1990
DESIGNER: SR MODELLER: RG
SIZE: 1 ¹/₂" x 1 ¹/₂" x 3"
ISSUE PRICE: £9.95

THE MISCHIEVOUS GOBLIN

T his study (nicknamed 'The Stumpy Goblin' by certain persons within The Tudor Mint!) was originally issued with the goblin's stick all the way down to the ground (Mould 1) but, as it kept breaking, it was quickly redesigned to rest on a tree knot (Mould 2) .

CODE: 3018
ISSUED: May 1989
RETIRED: December 1990
DESIGNER: SR MODELLER: RG/ML
SIZE: 2 ¹/₂" x 1" x 3"
ISSUE PRICE: £9.95

THE GORGON MEDUSA

A nother figurine inspired by Greek mythology: it is said that if one looked directly at the Gorgon one would be turned into a lump of stone. Mark Locker actually sculpted the original version (Mould 1) which was cast in three separate pieces; then Roger Gibbons remodelled the study as one whole piece, lowering the Gorgon's tail in the process and also enlarging her bust measurement by a cup size or two (Mould 2)!

Mould 2   Mould 1

55

THE ALCHEMIST ▶

CODE: 3019
ISSUED: May 1989
RETIRED: December 1990
DESIGNER: SR MODELLER: RG (ML)
SIZE: 1 ¹/₄" x 2" x 3 ¹/₂"
ISSUE PRICE: £9.95

The third of the red-bead studies, The Alchemist can be seen at his task of turning base metals into gold. In the red-bead version (Mould 1), the bead was intended to represent a vivid red potion; the change to a crystal (Mould 2) turned his recipe into a multi-coloured concoction! Though the nameplate does not reflect it, Mark Locker had a hand in both this and the next study, The Merman.

CODE: 3020
ISSUED: May 1989
RETIRED: December 1990
DESIGNER: SR MODELLER: RG (ML)
SIZE: 1 ¹/₂" x 1 ¹/₄" x 3 ³/₄"
ISSUE PRICE: £9.95

Mould 1   Mould 2

◀ THE MERMAN

In the early version the Merman holds his hand curled slightly (Mould 1), whilst in the later issues it is flat (Mould 2). The change was made because the crystal kept falling off.

THE MINOTAUR

In Greek mythology, The Minotaur had the rather unsociable habit of eating human flesh. Perhaps this accounts for the characteristic unique amongst the early figurines — his blood red (painted) eyes. Although the Minotaur's staff appears lengthened in later editions, and is less perpendicular to the base, this was due to a slight realignment of the crystal and is not a mould variation as such. An original version by Mark Locker was remodelled from scratch by Roger Gibbons prior to production.

CODE: 3022
ISSUED: May 1989
RETIRED: December 1991
DESIGNER: SR MODELLER: RG
SIZE: 1³/₄" x 1¹/₄" x 3¹/₂"
ISSUE PRICE: £9.95

THE DRAGON'S KISS

Mould 2   *Mould 1*

The dragon's kiss is incomplete in Mould 1 of this study, as the dragon and maiden's heads do not touch. This was corrected in the later Mould 2 version, when the study was also remodelled in one piece.

CODE: 3030
ISSUED: August 1989
RETIRED: December 1993
DESIGNER: SR MODELLER: RG (ML)
SIZE: 2 ¹/₂" x 2" x 2 ³/₄"
ISSUE PRICE: £9.95

WITCH AND ▶ FAMILIAR

The only study in the collection featuring a cat, which is seen pawing at the crystal. The study was relatively unpopular (witches are nowhere near as popular as wizards in the *Myth and Magic* range), and was only available for just over a year. No mould variations exist.

CODE: 3031
ISSUED: August 1989
RETIRED: December 1990
DESIGNER: SR MODELLER: RG
SIZE: 2" x 2" x 3 ¹/₂"
ISSUE PRICE: £9.95

CODE: 3032
ISSUED: August 1989
RETIRED: December 1993
DESIGNER: SR MODELLER: RG (ML)
SIZE: 1 ³/₄" x 1 ¹/₄" x 3 ¹/₂"
ISSUE PRICE: £9.95

THE ORIENTAL DRAGON

In Mould 1 of this study the first the wings were added separately to the dragon's back, but this was soon restyled so that the wings were integrated into the body (Mould 2). Another Mark Locker/Roger Gibbons collaboration — Mark sculpting the original and Roger the restyling.

THE FIRE DRAGON

CODE: 3034
ISSUED: August 1989
RETIRED: December 1993
DESIGNER: SR MODELLER: RG (ML)
SIZE: 2" x 1 ½" x 3"
ISSUE PRICE: £9.95

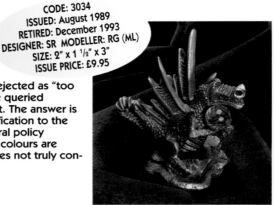

Sharon Riley's design featured a more skeletal dragon, but it was rejected as "too frightening"! Some collectors have queried whether two versions of the study exist. The answer is yes and no: yes, there was slight modification to the angle of the crystal, in line with a general policy change to position crystals so that the colours are more visible from the front; no, this does not truly constitute a remodelling as such.

CODE: 3035
ISSUED: August 1989
RETIRED: December 1993
DESIGNER: SR MODELLER: RG/ML
SIZE: 1 ¾" x 1 ½" x 4 ¼"
ISSUE PRICE: £9.95

THE GIANT SORCEROR

The Giant Sorceror was originally to be called The Mystical Sorceror, and the prototype at The Tudor Mint has this name on the baseplate. However, Sharon Riley's design drawing for the piece just happened to be larger than usual; when Roger Gibbons saw it, he assumed the study itself was to be larger and sculpted his model accordingly, thus making it larger in scale than most standard-sized studies. For this reason, when Graham Hughes saw the finished model he named it The Giant Sorceror. This had its own problems, for the Sorceror was to appear with his right arm raised aloft, shining forth the crystal (Mould 1). Unfortunately this meant that the study was too large to fit into the box, so the arm was lowered almost immediately in production to cradle the crystal (Mould 2). The modification was made by Mark Locker. Needless to say, 'arm up' versions are very rare, 'arm down' versions are not.

CODE: 3037
ISSUED: August 1989
RETIRED: December 1991
DESIGNER: SR MODELLER: RG (ML)
SIZE: 2 ¼" x 1 ½" x 3"
ISSUE PRICE: £9.95

THE LIGHT OF KNOWLEDGE ▶

In The Tudor Mint's Soldering Department, all manner of slight variations may occur (hats and arms at different angles, for example), as the studies are assembled by hand by a dozen or so artisans. The Light of Knowledge was prone to such slight alterations as much as any other, and a number have been reported. Nevertheless, no genuine remodelling took place during its production span. This is another example of a study which Mark Locker worked on uncredited.

THE EARTH WIZARD ▶

The Elemental Wizards, as they are known, form a mini-grouping of their own. Although The Earth Wizard's staff varies in position and angle, this is due to assembly variations, and not to mould modifications. Prices vary, however, depending on the type of crystal; the most sought-after are those with cubic or conical crystals. In praise of his prominent headdress, The Earth Wizard is known amongst the Tudor Mint model makers as The Onion Bhajee.

CODE: 3039
ISSUED: January 1990
RETIRED: December 1991
DESIGNER: SR MODELLER: RG (ML)
SIZE: 2" x 1 ¹/₂" x 3 ¹/₂"
ISSUE PRICE: £10.95

CODE: 3041
ISSUED: January 1990
RETIRED: December 1991
DESIGNER: SR MODELLER: RG
SIZE: 1 ³/₄" x 1 ¹/₂" x 3 ¹/₂"
ISSUE PRICE: £10.95

THE WATER WIZARD

The Water Wizard's watery provenance is shown by the shells and sea creatures that adorn his cloak, and the cup from which he drinks. This Wizard, too, is most sought after with a conical crystal.

THE AIR WIZARD

Known affectionately as Carmen Miranda by the model makers, due to The Air Wizard's ostentatious headgear (hers was made of fruit — his consists of feathers). Variations to the angle of the staff are not mould variations but the result of hand assembly in production. Prices vary on the secondary market according to the rarity of the crystal used.

CODE: 3042
ISSUED: January 1990
RETIRED: December 1991
DESIGNER: SR MODELLER: RG
SIZE: 1 ¹/₄" x 1 ¹/₄" x 3 ³/₄"
ISSUE PRICE: £10.95

CODE: 3044
ISSUED: January 1990
RETIRED: December 1993
DESIGNER: SR MODELLER: RG
SIZE: 3" x 2" x 3"
ISSUE PRICE: £15.35

THE DRAGON OF THE LAKE

A study which frequently appears with a cubic crystal, The Dragon of the Lake was the only one of the studies issued in January 1990 featuring a dragon on its own — and indeed was only the fifth so to do (another interesting bit of trivia!).

CODE: 3045
ISSUED: January 1990
RETIRED: December 1992
DESIGNER: SR MODELLER: RG (ML)
SIZE: 2 1/4" x 1 1/4" x 3 1/2"
ISSUE PRICE: £10.95

THE DRAGON'S SPELL

A study which suffers something of an identity crisis: usually referred to as 'The Dragon Spell' by The Tudor Mint, the nameplate insists it should be 'The Dragon's Spell'. In fact, the spell is of course the wizard's, as the 'dragon' is really a plinth in the shape of a dragon.

GEORGE AND THE DRAGON

CODE: 3047
ISSUED: January 1990
RETIRED: December 1990
DESIGNER: SR MODELLER: RG
SIZE: 2 1/2" x 1 1/2" x 3"
ISSUE PRICE: £10.95

This was the reissue and redesign of the earlier Deadly Combat whose name was unpopular with collectors. It was the first release in the main collection of a 'Fantasy and Legend' study, but was fairly short-lived, collectors perhaps still not liking the idea of a dragon being slain. By 1992 this study was already selling for £175 ; a bargain by 1994 standards!

THE DRAGON OF THE SEA ▶

CODE: 3048
ISSUED: August 1990
RETIRED: December 1993
DESIGNER: SR MODELLER: RG
SIZE: 2 1/2" x 1 3/4" x 3 1/4"
ISSUE PRICE: £10.95

The Dragon of the Sea is lucky enough to have fins — so he is one of the few dragons who can breathe both in and out of water. He also has a cousin on The Dragon Master — note the similarity of the heads.

CODE: 3052
ISSUED: August 1990
RETIRED: December 1993
DESIGNER: SR MODELLER: RG
SIZE: 3 1/4" x 2 1/2" x 3 1/4"
ISSUE PRICE: £15.35

VIRGIN AND UNICORN

Unicorns will only submit to the will of a virgin — but unfortunately this can occasionally lead to the unicorn's undoing — as witnessed in this study, where the virgin waits to break off the creature's horn! The Virgin and the Unicorn was originally released with a cubic crystal. Some afficionados have commented on the similarity between the unicorn on this study and the smaller unicorn on Spirits of the Forest (3051). Hmm, now you come to mention it . . .

THE CASTLE OF SPIRES ▶

Collectors had been asking for another castle for the collection, and Jessica Watson responded with this design — a complex piece with many walkways and hidden passageways. Models with conical crystals (as pictured here) are highly collectable.

CODE: 3061
ISSUED: January 1991
RETIRED: December 1993
DESIGNER: JW MODELLER: AS
SIZE: 2 1/2" x 2" x 2 3/4"
ISSUE PRICE: £17.50

Retired Studies

THE CASTLE IN THE CLOUDS ▶

CODE: 3062
ISSUED: January 1991
RETIRED: December 1992
DESIGNER: JW MODELLER: AS
SIZE: 2 ¼" x 2 ¼" x 3 ¼"
ISSUE PRICE: £12.95

This is the only study of Jessica Watson's first designs to be withdrawn. It suffers perhaps from being one of the smaller castles (on a par with The Enchanted Castle), though its popularity on the secondary market is rapidly increasing.

CODE: 3067
ISSUED: August 1991
RETIRED: December 1993
DESIGNER: JW MODELLER: ML
SIZE: 3 ¼" x 2 ¼" x 2 ¾"
ISSUE PRICE: £17.50

OLD FATHER TIME

The position of the crystals — situated in a rather neat 'egg-timer' — seem to vary with almost every piece, due perhaps to the awkwardness of getting them in place during assembly.

CODE: 3069
ISSUED: January 1992
RETIRED: December 1993
DESIGNER: JW MODELLER: AS
SIZE: 2" x 1 ½" x 3 ½"
ISSUE PRICE: £13.95

THE FAIRY QUEEN

Although female figurines tend to be less popular with collectors, two appeared at the same time in 1992. The Fairy Queen, like The Moon Wizard, is adorned with a red stone.

LARGER SIZE

CODE: 3303
(originally 3026)
ISSUED: January 1990
RETIRED: December 1993
DESIGNER: SR MODELLER: RG (ML)
SIZE: 4 ¹/₂" x 3" x 3 ¹/₂"
ISSUE PRICE: £34.95

SUMMONING THE ELEMENTS

O riginally issued in the standard-sized series as number 3026, then reissued with a wooden plinth as 3303. In Mould 1 the crystal mount was thinner and the crystal itself was clear. Unfortunately it was possible to see a rather murky glue holding it onto the font, and so for Mould 2 the type and colour of the crystal was changed to blue. Also for Mould 2 the wizard's arm and his staff were strengthened and thickened. A further alteration was made for Mould 3, where the lip at the top of the font was made more fluted.

Sharon Riley's original design featured three smaller crystals instead of one large, the font was more of a column, and the wizard's stance was more tempestuous, with swirling hair. Once produced, however, the prototype wizard was soon christened 'werewolf' — and he received the wizard equivalent of a short-back-and-sides for the version finally issued. Interestingly, the prototype wizard has long since disappeared from the Tudor Mint's store cupboard — perhaps the present owner should keep a silver bullet or two handy, just in case.

Summoning the Elements

THE SORCEROR'S APPRENTICE

Inspired by Sharon Riley's interest in the Arthurian sagas, this study calls to mind images such as those from Walt Disney's Fantasia. In Mould 1, the wall surrounding the fireplace was squared-off, but to give the study more life, Mould 2's walls are jagged and wider.

THE NEST OF DRAGONS

In retrospect, Sharon Riley wishes she had been able to devote more time to this study in order to perfect her design. Nevertheless it was popular with collectors and sold well up until its retirement. Despite the name plate credit, this piece was sculpted by Mark Locker.

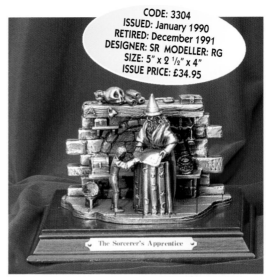

CODE: 3304
ISSUED: January 1990
RETIRED: December 1991
DESIGNER: SR MODELLER: RG
SIZE: 5" x 2 ½" x 4"
ISSUE PRICE: £34.95

The Sorceror's Apprentice

CODE: 3305
ISSUED: January 1990
RETIRED: December 1993
DESIGNER: SR MODELLER: RG (ML)
SIZE: 4 ¾" x 2½" x 3 ¼"
ISSUE PRICE: £34.95

The Nest of Dragons

SENTINELS AT THE PORTAL

The Portal in question is the door to the underworld. A resemblance between the sentinels and The Grim Reaper is anything but coincidental. Watch out for a number of name variations: it should be 'Sentinels at the Portal', but 'The' is sometimes added, plurals added or subtracted — all sorts.

CODE: 3307
ISSUED: January 1990
Retired: December 1991
DESIGNER: SR MODELLER: RG (ML)
SIZE: 5" x 2 ½" x 4"
ISSUE PRICE: £34.95

The Sentinels at the Portal

THE DANCE OF THE DOLPHINS
(Limited Edition)

CODE: 3311
ISSUED: August 1990
RETIRED: December 1993
EDITION SIZE: 7500 - but see below
DESIGNER: SR MODELLER: RG
SIZE: 8" x 8 ½" x 9"
ISSUE PRICE: £175

T he third limited edition study proved to be the least popular. The edition size was intended to be 7,500 but the piece was retired due to lack of demand and eventually replaced by the smaller 'Playful Dolphins'. By the summer of 1992 sales had reached 1,497, but a year later only a further 40 had been ordered, and so the decision was made to retire it at the end of 1993. The study depicts seven dolphins 'dancing' around a mermaid who sits atop the ruins of a great city under the sea.

The Myth and Magic Collectors Club

The Myth and Magic Collectors Club was formed on 1st May 1990 to offer news and information to the rapidly growing throng of enthusiasts, and also to provide special pieces available exclusively to Club members. For the first year, membership was restricted to the UK only, but the Club went "World Wide" on 1st May 1991. Originally annual membership ran from 1st May until 30th April, but this was changed in 1992/93, when the club year was extended until 30th June 1993. It now runs from 1st July until 30th June each year.

Every year membership entitles you to a free study — the Collectors Club Annual Presentation Piece — plus the option (but not the obligation) to purchase two Members Only studies. There is also a regular newsletter, The Methtintdour Times, which is mailed direct to collectors and contains details about new products, stories about the studies, background information and prize competitions. From 1990 until 1992, three 8-page issues a year were produced, but this was changed in the spring of 1993 to two 12-pages issues. (Anyone who spends a lot of money on stamps will understand why!)

Part of the fun of collecting is being part of a group of like-minded collectors, and the easiest way to do this is by joining the Collectors Club. And the fact that membership of the Club has a kind of built-in 'investment value' is a very pleasant bonus.

STEPHANIE OSBORNE

From the beginning, the Club has been administered chiefly by Stephanie Osborne. She is the ideal person for the task — not only is she an excellent administrator, but she has also worked in just about every department of W.A.P. Watson Ltd. and can tell you anything you might wish to know about *Myth and Magic* . . . and every other product. Should you wish to meet her in person, Stephanie attends all the promotions at which Exhibition Only studies are sold. When she isn't working, she enjoys horse riding, gardening, dog walking and reading. And beware of what you say in her presence about the Windsors; she is a great fan of the Royal Family.

Amongst the facts and figures Stephanie has at her fingertips are a few less conventional but no less interesting gems. For example, she can tell you that on the whole, women prefer studies that feature unicorns, Pegasus and 'cute' dragons; whereas men tend to go for fierce-looking dragons.

ALLAN FROST

Together with Stephanie Osborne, Allan Frost, to many, is the human face of The Tudor Mint, primarily as Editor of the Collectors Club newsletter, The Methtintdour Times. Yet surprisingly, Allan is not an employee of The Tudor Mint. He is, as he states, "a collector who offered help." He fell under the *Myth and*

Magic spell whilst shopping in the Shropshire town of Wellington. In a shop window he saw The Book of Spells . . . and was captivated. He had always had an interest in dragons and wizards (inspired perhaps by living close to the Welsh borderland) and was soon carrying home some new purchases. "It was rare to find the combination of excellent craftsmanship and reasonable prices," he says. "I joined the Collectors Club almost immediately."

Allan's offer of help followed a phone call to Stephanie at The Tudor Mint to enquire if they would be sending a newsletter. The reply was that they did not have a newsletter. "Why not do one?" Allan thought to himself, and within days he had sent his draft — by now christened The Methtintdour Times (Allan is anagram-mad!) — to The Tudor Mint. Soon he was discussing the idea with Graham Hughes, and 'Issue Number 1' was published that summer (1990).

Perhaps Allan's greatest contribution to *Myth and Magic* is that he has created a land for the wizards, dragons and mythical beasts to inhabit. Methtintdour is his own invention, so too are the many stories he has developed to enhance the studies; they can be read in The Methtintdour Times. In 1991 he went a step further and wrote a fantasy novel — The Stracyl of Unity — which is set in the land of Methtintdour. The book was published by The Tudor Mint. Allan, let it be known, also invented The Game of Strax!

ANNUAL PRESENTATION PIECES

Annual Presentation Pieces are the complimentary studies given by The Tudor Mint to collectors who join the Myth and Magic Collectors Club. A new study is offered for each membership year and is delivered direct from the Club office to Club members. Whilst current, these studies cannot be purchased in shops and do not have an initial quotable value. However, immediately on retirement, they become available on the secondary market at a far greater value than the Club membership fee and thus represent extremely good investments.

Typical base marking: MYTH AND MAGIC COLLECTORS CLUB   MEMBERSHIP STUDY 1994-1995 THE DREAMY DRAGON BY Mark Locker CC05 WAPW © U.K.

CODE: CC01
ISSUED: May 1990
RETIRED: April 1991
DESIGNER: SR MODELLER: RG
SIZE: 2 ½" x 1 ½" x 3"
ISSUE PRICE: NIL

THE PROTECTOR

Membership of the Club for the year 1990/91 was restricted to the UK only and cost £10. 8,849 'Protectors' were produced. During 1992 they were already selling for £150: the value has almost doubled again since then. The study depicts Snowscale with her son, the dragonet Tomepicker, both characters in Allan Frost's novel The Stracyl of Unity. This is Stephanie Osborne's favourite piece — for purely material reasons, because she has one!

Collectors Club

THE JOVIAL WIZARD

CODE: CC02
ISSUED: May 1991
RETIRED: April 1992
DESIGNER: JW MODELLER: ML
SIZE: 2" x 2 ¾" x 3 ¼"
ISSUE PRICE: NIL

I n 1991/92 Club membership increased to £12.95 – remarkable value compared with the current value of the free study which members received — and for the first time membership was available in the USA. By the end of the Club year, The Tudor Mint had produced and delivered 11,679 'Jovial Wizards', reflecting a considerable increase in membership on the previous year. The Jovial Wizard in question is Tankar, a wizard renowned for his knowledge of (and consumption of) good ale. For Mould 2 the chair on this study was strengthened at the top and was also hollowed out; this took place fairly early into production (summer 1991).

THE DRAGON OF DESTINY

CODE: CC03
ISSUED: May 1992
RETIRED: June 1993
DESIGNER: SR MODELLER: RG
SIZE: 2½" x 2 ¼" x 2 ¾"
ISSUE PRICE: NIL

I n the 1992/93 year it was decided to extend the Club membership period to 30th June, to fall in line with The Tudor Mint production schedule, which usually releases new studies in January and August of each year. Membership increased to £13.95 for the extended year, and despite its longer availability period, The Dragon of Destiny has, like its predecessors, proved a star performer on the secondary market. The Dragon of Destiny, in the lore of the Elves, holds the world in its position in the heavens. It is he who controls the weather, breathing fire for heat, issuing forth steam for rain.

THE DRAGON OF METHTINTDOUR ▶

M embership for the 1993/94 year increased to £14.95. The Dragon of Methtintdour is Skyview, who allowed Contaur the wizard to ride on his back — the first dragon to allow himself to be ridden by another creature. In the study he is seen sitting on the map of Methtintdour.

CODE: CC04
ISSUED: July 1993
RETIRED: June 1994
DESIGNER: SR MODELLER: AS
SIZE: 2 ½" x 3" x 3"
ISSUE PRICE: NIL

Collectors Club

THE DREAMY DRAGON

CODE: CC05
ISSUED: July 1994
RETIRED: June 1995
DESIGNER: SR MODELLER: ML
SIZE: 2 ½" x 1 ¾" x 3"
ISSUE PRICE: NIL

Dreamy indeed, as the dragon dozes on a majestic rocking chair. When first cast, the solid nature of the study made it rather weighty, and so (prior to release) the chair was lowered and hollowed out. For the 1994/95 Club season, membership remained the same as 1993/94 — £14.95.

MEMBERS ONLY STUDIES

The Tudor Mint produce two Members Only studies each year available solely to members of the Collectors Club. They are obtained via a card which is taken to the member's retailer who places an order with The Tudor Mint. This ensures that only members can buy and that each member only purchases one piece.

The first of the two annual Members Only studies appears at the beginning of the Club year — around July — and the other in the middle — January-ish.

Members Only studies are lower in edition size, and therefore rarer even than Annual Presentation pieces as not all members take up the invitation to buy. For example, of the 8,849 members of the 1990/91 Club, less than a quarter chose to purchase Quest for the Truth. Consequently these studies are much sought-after, especially by new collectors.

Members who joined the Club in 1990/91 are classified as Founder Members and are entitled to keep their original Club membership number. As a matter of interest, there are two Honorary members: George Atkinson, The Tudor Mint's ex-Sales Manager who was prominent in developing the *Myth and Magic* range, and Jean Knowles, the Home Sales Office Manageress who retired just when the Club was being formed; she was also given Membership Number One.

The current policy is to release one standard-sized and one larger study (with wooden plinth) each year.

Typical base marking: MYTH AND MAGIC COLLECTORS CLUB RESTRICTED AVAILABILITY STUDY 1993-1994 THE MYSTICAL ENCOUNTER BY A.G. Slocombe WAPW © U.K. 9007

THE QUEST FOR THE TRUTH

CODE: 9001
ISSUED: August 1990
RETIRED: April 1991
DESIGNER: SR MODELLER: RG (ML)
SIZE: 4 ¾" x 2¾"x4"
ISSUE PRICE: £49.95

Only 1,282 'Quests' were released by The Tudor Mint. Just nine were produced with a green (Sahara) crystal, three of which went to the USA; the crystal was then changed to blue (Bermuda). In Mould 2 the wizard's hand was curled into a fist, as he had a tendency to lose his (pointing) index finger during polishing, and the wizard and dragon were cast separately, instead of as one.

The Quest for the Truth

Collectors Club

THE GAME OF STRAX

As many frustrated Extravaganza attendees will tell you, The Game of Strax is neither the easiest game to play nor the easiest piece to buy. The game itself was devised by Allan Frost, and is not dissimilar to the French game 'boules'. 2,533 were sold and thus rarity value is reflected in its current valuation.

THE WELL OF ASPIRATIONS

This study was originally issued with the winch handle extending horizontally and a longer hook hanging

above the well, but so many were damaged in transit that the design was changed. For Mould 2 the handle hung vertically and the hook was shortened. In total, 2,973 were made. If you look carefully, somewhere on the well you will find the inscription 'JOS' — the initials of modeller Anthony Slocombe's son Jack. Allan Frost says: "I came up with the name 'Well of Aspirations' when George Atkinson phoned to say he wanted a title something like 'The Wishing Well' but not so obvious. This was the best I could do." And it does very well.

PLAYMATES ▶

Some have wondered how a cherub fits into the collection — and the answer may lie in the fact that at the time of design, Sharon Riley's son Daniel had just been born. Sharon admits he was a big baby, but this was not the reason for the prototype having a rather long and fat right arm, which was later corrected (or for that matter why the cherub has wings)! During the four months it was available, 3,778 'Playmates' were sold. One prototype (with Certificate of Authenticity) was sent to a renewing Collectors Club member at random, minus the baseplate.

FRIENDS

Six prototypes were made with the wings on the wrong way round, but none was released onto the market.

CODE: 9005
ISSUED: July 1992
RETIRED: June 1993
DESIGNER: SR MODELLER: AS
SIZE: 2 ¼" x 2 ¼" x 3 ½"
ISSUE PRICE: £18.95

THE ENCHANTED POOL

Production of this study was merrily under way when someone in 'Casting' at The Tudor Mint (Dawn Ward) noticed that the wizard was deficient in the foot department to the tune of one — in other words, his right foot was missing (Mould 1)! In fact, the wizard did look the way Roger Gibbons had intended — "the other foot's under his cloak," he claims. Nevertheless, a hasty modification was made (Mould 2). The precise number of monoped versions is unknown but the mistake was noticed early in production and the quantity is rumoured to be about fifty. The Tudor Mint released a fascinating video based upon the story behind this study, which also explains the manufacturing process; see Memorabilia section.

CODE: 9006
ISSUED: November 1992
RETIRED: June 1993
DESIGNER: JW MODELLER: RG
SIZE: 5" x 3 ½" x 3"
ISSUE PRICE: £49.95

THE MYSTICAL ENCOUNTER

The Tudor Mint knew that unicorns and dragons are popular subjects with collectors, and so they decided it would be an added bonus to combine the two on The Mystical Encounter. The study proved troublesome in transit: the unicorn kept losing its horn. To circumvent the problem a 'blob' of polystyrene was used to cover the horn when it was mailed.

CODE: 9007
ISSUED: August 1993
RETIRED: June 1994
DESIGNER: SR MODELLER: AS
SIZE: 3 ½" x 2 ½" x 3"
ISSUE PRICE: £19.75

THE KEEPER OF THE DRAGONS

CODE: 9008
ISSUED: January 1994
RETIRED: June 1994
DESIGNER: SR MODELLER: RG
SIZE: 5" x 2 ½" x 4"
ISSUE PRICE: £49.95

If there's one thing more popular than unicorns and dragons it's wizards and dragons — and The Keeper of the Dragons combines the two. (How long, it may be asked, until we get a piece featuring unicorns, dragons and wizards!) The crystal tended to snap off on the first few production runs at The Tudor Mint, and so the stone was given a mount; at the same time the crystal was also changed. The study was issued initially with a brass name plate for the plinth; this was changed in March 1994 to an iron one, to fit in with the rest of the Collectors Club studies.

THE BATTLE FOR THE CRYSTAL

CODE: 9010
ISSUED: August 1994
RETIRED: June 1995
DESIGNER: SR MODELLER: AS

The second Members Only study for 1994-1995, available between January and June 1995. This is Sharon Riley's design drawing.

THE CRYSTAL SHIELD ▼

The first Members Only study for 1994-1995, available between August 1994 and June 1995.

CODE: 9009
ISSUED: August 1994
RETIRED: June 1995
DESIGNER: SR MODELLER: ML
SIZE: 3 ¼" x 2 x 3 ½"
ISSUE PRICE: £19.95

Crystals and Stones

Listed here are the major shapes, sizes and colours of crystals used by The Tudor Mint up until summer 1994. The list is not exhaustive and does not include new crystals being introduced on studies from July 1994 onwards.

Crystal Colours

Aquamarine
Pale blue
Rare - used on perhaps 1 in 30 models.

Aurora Borealis
Multicoloured/cloudy (colours appear to be on surface of crystal)
Rare - found on early pieces (e.g. The Protector) but no longer in use.

Bermuda Blue
Deep blue
Commonly found on early models but no longer used.

Crystal
Clear
Rarely used

Heliotrope
Mauve/pinky-blue
Rare - used only in small quantities.

Light Vitrail
Pale multicoloured
Rarely found

Medium Vitrail
Rainbow/multicoloured
Found on most studies - the most commonly used.

New Bermuda Blue
Bluey green
Used now as a replacement for Bermuda Blue, but has a slightly greener hue.

Sahara
Greeny gold
The rarest of all - very few ever used.

Crystal Shapes

Conical
Sizes Used: 8, 12, 14 mm
Commonly found on early models; still used but very infrequently.

Cubic
Sizes Used: 8, 12, 14 mm
Commonly found on early models; no longer used.

Global-shaped
Sizes Used: 8, 12, 14 mm
Most commonly used of all (rarer are the global crystals with large facets, known as 'football' crystals).

Pear-shaped
Sizes Used: 35x20, 50x30 mm
Regularly used, mainly on larger studies or for special effect.

STONES

In addition to the main crystals found on studies, a variety of additional smaller stones are also used to create special effects — such as dragons' eyes (Smaug the Dragon, The Power of the Crystal), and decoration for shields (Sir Mordred, Return of Excalibur).

Limited Availability Studies

Availability of the studies listed in this section is restricted by a time period (as are Collectors Club pieces). Studies limited by edition size are listed in the Current or Retired groupings.

ONE YEAR ONLY STUDIES

Not all *Myth and Magic* collectors necessarily want to join the Collectors Club, and so the One Year Only studies were introduced to provide everyone, including non-members, with an opportunity to purchase a special study with restricted availability. A new study is released each year and is available from 1st January to 31st December when it is retired and replaced by a new study. It should be remembered that although The Tudor Mint cease making the One Year Only studies at that time, stocks may remain in shops into the New Year. Nevertheless, immediately on retirement (1st January), their secondary market value increases beyond the List Price.

Typical base marking: 1993 "ONE YEAR ONLY" PIECE THE FLYING DRAGON BY A.G. Slocombe OY93 WAPW © MADE IN THE U.K.

THE FLYING DRAGON

Jessica Watson's design of a dragon launching itself from a rock altered dramatically during Anthony Slocombe's modelling. Soon after issue, it was noted by a collector that (in the words of The Tudor Mint) " . . . one of the rocky outcrops on the base looked embarrassingly like a part of the human (male) anatomy!" The study was hastily remodelled, and, as you would imagine, the original 300 are now sought after.

CODE: OY93
ISSUED: January 1993
RETIRED: December 1993
DESIGNER: JW MODELLER: AS
SIZE: 5 ¼" x 3 ½" x 2 ½"
ISSUE PRICE: £39.95

THE DRAGON OF THE UNDERWORLD

CODE: OY94
ISSUED: January 1994
RETIRED: December 1994
DESIGNER: SR MODELLER: RG
SIZE: 3" x 2 ½" x 5 ½"
ISSUE PRICE: £41.50

One of Sharon Riley's favourite designs, and one that remained close to her original drawing. The dragon is shown protecting the crystal housed in the pillar. In Mould 1 the stone had no mount and the wings above the dragon's head stood parallel with each other, without touching. In Mould 2 the wings were remodelled (April '94) in order to touch slightly, and the mount for the crystal was also changed.

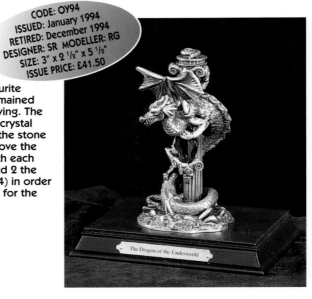

The Dragon of the Underworld

THE GUARDIAN OF THE CRYSTAL

A fine example of the new generation of studies in which larger crystals become a more prominent feature. This picture of The Guardian of the Crystal is something of a coup (courtesy of The Tudor Mint), as the study will not be available until six months after the book has been published. When released in January 1995, the study will be supplied with a wooden plinth.

CODE: OY95
ISSUED: January 1995
RETIRED: December 1995
DESIGNER: SR MODELLER: AS
SIZE: 2 ¾" x 2 ½" x 5 ½"
ISSUE PRICE: £49.95

EXTRAVAGANZA *STUDIES*

The idea of a get-together for collectors was initiated by Graham Hughes after experiencing conventions in the USA, and the first 'Extravaganza' took place in September 1991. Those lucky enough to attend (over 800 people) were able to see talks, shows, exhibitions, and to take part in draws, quizzes and The Game of Strax. They were also issued with the first Extravaganza Drout (see Memorabilia section). The event was such a success that it is now held annually.

What made the 1992 Extravaganza especially different from the first was the availability for those who attended of Sauria, the Extravaganza Special Piece — a study available only to those who could make it to the event. The 1993 event continued this newly created tradition with Deinos, and 1994 brings yet another chance for collectors to get together and enjoy their communal interest, not to mention purchase Lithia!

Typical base marking: MYTH AND MAGIC COLLECTORS CLUB "SAURIA" BY A.G. Slocombe 1992-1993 EXTRAVAGANZA ONLY STUDY WAPW © U.K.

CODE: 3600
ISSUED: October 1992
RETIRED: October 1992
DESIGNER: SR MODELLER: AS
SIZE: 2" x 2" x 4 ¼"
ISSUE PRICE: £19.95

SAURIA

Only 403 Sauria's were issued, and in a little under two years the value has risen fifteen-fold from its original selling price — a pretty good investment! Graham Hughes admits to a particular affection for the first Extravaganza study and Sauria is the only piece of *Myth and Magic* which he has at home.

DEINOS

When combined, the names of the first two Extravaganza studies create another name (give or take a few letters), that of a famous prehistoric animal, which translates into English as "terrible lizard". So the 1993 Extravaganza piece was called 'Terrible!' Fortunately its appearance does not match its name. Only 463 were made - and within a year of issue the value of the study has increased almost twenty-fold.

CODE: 3602
ISSUED: September 1993
RETIRED: September 1993
DESIGNER: JW MODELLER: RG
SIZE: 3" x 2" x 4 ¹/₄"
ISSUE PRICE: £19.95

CODE: 3604
ISSUED: September 1994
RETIRED: September 1994
DESIGNER: SR MODELLER: ML
SIZE: 2" x 2" x 4" (approx.)
ISSUE PRICE: £19.95

LITHIA

Sharon Riley's turn again to design the Extravaganza study — she and Jessica Watson seem to be taking turns. Her 1994 piece features her fondness for long, curling dragon's tails. The name of the study derives from 'Lithium', the lightest of all metals. Pictured here is Sharon's design illustration from which Mark Locker modelled the finished study.

EXHIBITION *ONLY* STUDIES

Exhibitions (a mixture of demonstration and promotion) are held by The Tudor Mint about six times a year, each in a different area of the UK and in conjunction with one of their nominated stockists. Exhibition Only studies were introduced in 1993 primarily to accommodate those collectors who were unable to attend the Extravaganzas — and like Extravaganza, they offer the chance to purchase a special study. The 1993 piece was Dactrius, and the 1994 piece is Vexius. The promotions are attended by Stephanie Osborne (Collectors Club) and Malcolm Crewdson (Master Mould Maker), and in 1993 included several in Canada (Toronto area) as well in the UK. So far all the Exhibition and Extravaganza studies have been 'named' pieces — in other words, they are not 'The Dragon of' etc. but have specific titles.

Typical base marking: 1994 EXHIBITION ONLY PIECE VEXIUS BY A.G. Slocombe WAPW © MADE IN THE U.K. (though on Dactrius three sculptors are credited).

DACTRIUS

Dactrius is unique in that he was sculpted jointly by Roger Gibbons, Mark Locker and Anthony Slocombe (the intention being that at least one sculptor could attend each demonstration and sign the special certificate which comes with every model). The name 'Dactrius' is extracted from a real winged serpent, the pterodactyl. On the first pieces to be cast (Mould 1), the dragon's chin was not attached to its wing, but the model was altered so that chin and wing were touching for greater strength (Mould 2).

CODE: 3601
ISSUED: March 1993
RETIRED: November 1993
DESIGNER: SR MODELLER: RG/ML/AS
SIZE: 3¼" x 2¼" x 5"
ISSUE PRICE: £39.95

Dactrius

VEXIUS

CODE: 3603
ISSUED: February 1994
RETIRED: November 1994
DESIGNER: JW MODELLER: AS
SIZE: 4" x 3" x 5 ¼"
ISSUE PRICE: £41.50

Some names come naturally, others have to be worked at. When all you can do is sit around wondering what to name a new study, the only solution is to say: "It's vexed us." And the rest, as they say, is history. Mould 1 had wings joined to the body separately and the candelabra was thinner. In Mould 2 (April 1994) the wings were cast with the body as one, the candelabra was thickened to stop it breaking, and the pots were filled in.

Other Collections

THE J.R.R. TOLKIEN COLLECTION
(THE HOBBIT & LORD OF THE RINGS COLLECTIONS)

I f ever a collection can be said to be "in response to the demands of our collectors" then this is it. When the Myth and Magic Collectors Club was launched, application forms to join included a questionnaire asking for suggestions for new studies. Nine out of ten replies to the Club office wanted figurines based on the stories of J.R.R. Tolkien.

THE HOBBIT COLLECTION

The Hobbit Collection appeared in the summer of 1991 after some drawn-out negotiations between The Tudor Mint and Tolkien Enterprises of Berkeley, California, USA, who own the copyright to the Tolkien stories. The collection consists of twenty-four characters and scenes from Tolkien's book *The Hobbit;* all were designed by Jessica Watson, who confesses that her research even included reading comic-strip versions of the story!

In effect *The Hobbit Collection* is now retired. However, three of the twenty-four studies (Bilbo Baggins, Gandalf and Gollum) are still available but have been absorbed

into *The Lord of the Rings Collection* with a new backstamp and packaging.

Individual prices can be found in Section Three. However, it may be of interest to know that during 1993 a complete set of The Hobbit Collection (5001 to 5024) was sold for a figure in the region of £3,500.

Typical base marking: THE HOBBIT COLLECTION NO.1 OF A SERIES OF 24 "BILBO BAGGINS" U.K. 5001 © TOLKIEN ENT. 1991 (Sculptors are not credited on baseplates in this collection, but some of the studies are signed on the piece itself, usually at the back.)

BILBO BAGGINS

A Hobbit who enjoys a comfortable life. Notice his furry feet. 'Bilbo' was rereleased in January 1994 with a *Lord of the Rings* backstamp and packaging. The original *Hobbit* backstamp version has already acquired a secondary market value of double the issue price. Claims have been made that Bilbo resembles a number of people (comedian Charlie Drake, and a salesperson at The Tudor Mint amongst them), but Jessica Watson insists that her characterisation is pure fantasy.

CODE: 5001
ISSUED: August 1991
DESIGNER: JW MODELLER: RG
SIZE: 2" x 2" x 3"
ISSUE PRICE: £13.95

CODE: 5002
ISSUED: August 1991
DESIGNER: JW MODELLER: AS
SIZE: 2³/₄" x 1³/₄" x 4¹/₄"
ISSUE PRICE: £24.95

GANDALF

A wizard — an excellent maker of fireworks — held in awe by many. Rereleased in January 1994 with a *Lord of the Rings* backstamp and packaging.

THORIN OAKENSHIELD

Son of a Dwarf King and leader of the dwarves — a very important dwarf indeed.

CODE: 5003
ISSUED: August 1991
RETIRED: December 1992
DESIGNER: JW MODELLER: RG
SIZE: 2" x 2" x 3 ¼"
ISSUE PRICE: £13.95

THE GREAT GOBLIN

A very nasty piece of work, slain by Gandalf and the sword Orchrist.

CODE: 5004
ISSUED: August 1991
RETIRED: December 1993
DESIGNER: JW MODELLER: RG
SIZE: 2¾" x 2" x 3 ½"
ISSUE PRICE: £13.95

CODE: 5005
ISSUED: August 1991
DESIGNER: JW MODELLER: AS
SIZE: 3 ¾" x 2 ¼" x 2 ½"
ISSUE PRICE: £17.50

CODE: 5006
ISSUED: August 1991
RETIRED: December 1992
DESIGNER: JW MODELLER: AS
SIZE: 3 ½" x 2 ¾" x 5"
ISSUE PRICE: £24.95

GOLLUM ▲

One of the three studies rereleased in January 1994 with a *Lord of the Rings* backstamp and packaging. The character Gollum was once a Hobbit, now a slimy creature who eats goblins and fish. He once owned The Ring — his 'precious'.

BEORN

The Skin Changer who can talk to animals and become a bear (see 5020)! Mould 1 has a shorter cloak; in Mould 2 it was lengthened to touch the log.

CODE: 5007
ISSUED: August 1991
RETIRED: December 1992
DESIGNER: JW MODELLER: AS
SIZE: 2½" x 1¾" x 3 ¾"
ISSUE PRICE: £17.50

THE ELVEN KING

He wears a variety of crowns corresponding with the woodland seasons; captor of Thorin and the dwarves.

CODE: 5008
ISSUED: August 1991
RETIRED: December 1993
DESIGNER: JW MODELLER: AS
SIZE: 6 ½" x 4 ½" x 2 ¾"
ISSUE PRICE: £54.95

◀ SMAUG THE DRAGON

T he mighty dragon who lives in the Lonely Mountain and is feared by all.

CODE: 5009
ISSUED: August 1991
RETIRED: December 1992
DESIGNER: JW MODELLER: ML
SIZE: 3" x 2" x 4"
ISSUE PRICE: £13.95

BARD

T he archer, who with his last black arrow kills mighty Smaug and becomes a hero.

CODE: 5010
ISSUED: August 1991
RETIRED: December 1993
DESIGNER: JW MODELLER: RG
SIZE: 4½" x 3" x 4 ¼"
ISSUE PRICE: £39.95

'GOOD MORNING' AT BAG END ▲

G andalf and Bilbo outside the comfortable Hobbit hole named Bag End.

MOON LETTERS

E lrond (half elven) at the Last Homely House deciphers moon-letters on the dwarves' map and identifies swords taken from the Trolls as 'goblin slayers.' One minor change was made to this study: the 'beer' in the mug was filled in on later issues.

CODE: 5011
ISSUED: August 1991
RETIRED: December 1992
DESIGNER: JW MODELLER: AS
SIZE: 4 ½" x 2 ½" x 4"
ISSUE PRICE: £54.95

FINDING THE 'PRECIOUS'

CODE: 5012
ISSUED: August 1991
RETIRED: December 1992
DESIGNER: JW MODELLER: RG
SIZE: 5" x 1 ½" x 2 ¾"
ISSUE PRICE: £39.95

Knocked uncon-
scious in his escape
from the goblins, Bilbo
finds The Ring and slips it in his pocket,
unaware of its magic powers.

CODE: 5013
ISSUED: August 1991
RETIRED: December 1992
DESIGNER: JW MODELLER: AS
SIZE: 4 ½" x 2 ¾" x 3 ½"
ISSUE PRICE: £39.95

THE CAPTURE OF BILBO ▲

Seeking shelter in a cave from a violent
thunderstorm, the company are cap-
tured by goblins, until Gandalf appears
and creates a fiery diversion.

CODE: 5014
ISSUED: August 1991
RETIRED: December 1992
DESIGNER: JW MODELLER: AS
SIZE: 4 ½" x 2" x 3"
ISSUE PRICE: £32.95

◀ 'RIDDLES IN THE DARK'

Bilbo and Gollum ask riddles
of each other. Should Gollum
win, he will eat Bilbo.
Should Bilbo win, then Gollum
will show him the way out of
the mountain.

CODE: 5016
ISSUED: August 1991
RETIRED: December 1992
DESIGNER: JW MODELLER: A
SIZE: 5" x 3" x 4"
ISSUE PRICE: £39.95

CODE: 5015
ISSUED: August 1991
RETIRED: December 1992
DESIGNER: JW MODELLER: RG
SIZE: 4 ½" x 2 ½" x 4 ¼"
ISSUE PRICE: £39.95

ESCAPE FROM THE WARGS

The dwarves are forced to escape up trees
when attacked by Wargs (wolves).

BARRELS OUT OF BOND ▲

At Bilbo's suggestion, the dwarves
escape from the elves in empty barrels which are floated down river.

CODE: 5017
ISSUED: August 1991
RETIRED: December 1992
DESIGNER: JW MODELLER: AS
SIZE: 5" x 3" x 2 ½"
ISSUE PRICE: £32.95

◀ 'THE COURAGE OF BILBO'

Attacked by a great spider, Bilbo kills the beast and names his sword 'Sting'.

CODE: 5018
ISSUED: August 1991
RETIRED: December 1992
DESIGNER: JW MODELLER: AS
SIZE: 2 ½" x 5" x 4"
ISSUE PRICE: £39.95

PRISONER OF THE ELVEN KING ▲

Captured by wood elves, Thorin refuses to reveal to the Elven King the reason for his journey.

THE WRATH OF BEORN ▼

During the Battle of Five Armies, Beorn appears as a bear and with the help of the eagles drives off the Goblins.

CODE: 5019
ISSUED: August 1991
RETIRED: December 1992
DESIGNER: JW MODELLER: ML
SIZE: 5" x 3" x 4"
ISSUE PRICE: £54.95

CODE: 5020
ISSUED: August 1991
RETIRED: December 1992
DESIGNER: JW MODELLER: ML
SIZE: 5" x 2 ½" x 4"
ISSUE PRICE: £39.95

THE ENCHANTED DOOR ▲

The company, with Thorin's key, open the door into the Lonely Mountain, the keyhole being lit by the rays of the setting sun as predicted in Moon-Letters (5011).

CODE: 5021
ISSUED: August 1991
RETIRED: December 1993
DESIGNER: JW MODELLER: RG
SIZE: 4" x 3" x 3 ½"
ISSUE PRICE: £39.95

JOURNEY'S END

Bilbo, after his many adventures, returns to his Hobbit Hole, puts his feet up and enjoys a smoke and a rest.

THE TROLL'S CLEARING

CODE: 5022
ISSUED: August 1991
RETIRED: December 1992
DESIGNER: JW MODELLER: RG
SIZE: 8" x 7 ¾" x 4 ¾"
ISSUE PRICE: £147.95

William, Bert and Tom are roasting mutton, much preferring manflesh, when Bilbo decides to prove his worth as a burglar!

CODE: 5023
ISSUED: August 1991
RETIRED: December 1993
DESIGNER: JW MODELLER: AS
SIZE: 8" x 7 ½" x 5"
ISSUE PRICE: £149.95

THE BURGLAR STEALS SMAUG'S GREAT CUP

Bilbo, wearing the ring, and so invisible, enters the mountain and to prove his worth to the dwarves, steals a great cup from Smaug's treasure. Mould 1 had a pillar at the front and to the right but it had a tendency to break off, and was thus removed for Mould 2. Also at this time the chalice that Bilbo holds was thickened as it used to break during polishing.

CODE: 5024
ISSUED: August 1991
RETIRED: December 1992
DESIGNER: JW MODELLER: ML
SIZE: 7 ½" x 6 ¾" x 4"
ISSUE PRICE: £149.95

FAREWELL, KING UNDER THE MOUNTAIN

The mortally injured Thorin lies with the Arkenstone on his breast, happy that he is reconciled with Bilbo. The pile of armour and baggage at the front of the study was larger in Mould 1; in Mould 2 it was reduced and integrated into the base. The setting for the stone on the chest was altered at this time.

THE LORD OF THE RINGS COLLECTION

All the *Lord of the Rings* studies remain available throughout 1994, with six scheduled for retirement on 31st December.

Typical base marking: THE LORD OF THE RINGS COLLECTION   FIRST SERIES   NO.4 OF A SERIES OF 12 "SAM GAMGEE"   U.K. 5028 © TOLKIEN ENT. 1991. (As with *The Hobbit Collection*, sculptors are not credited on baseplates, but some studies are signed on the actual piece.)

FRODO BAGGINS

CODE: 5025
ISSUED: January 1992
DESIGNER: JW MODELLER: RG
SIZE: 2¼" x 2¼" x 3"
ISSUE PRICE: £14.95

Bilbo's cousin, the only son of Drogo Baggins and Primula Brandybuck. Frodo's adventures and heroic deeds are numerous; during one of them his ring finger is bitten off by Gollum — hence his extended name, Frodo of the Nine Fingers.

CODE: 5026
ISSUED: January 1992
DESIGNER: JW MODELLER: ML
SIZE: 2¼" x 2" x 2½"
ISSUE PRICE: £14.95

CODE: 5027
ISSUED: January 1992
DESIGNER: JW MODELLER: ML
SIZE: 2¼" x 2" x 3¼"
ISSUE PRICE: £14.95

BILBO'S TALE ▲

Amongst other things, Bilbo Baggins is an author, scholar and a poet. Here he sits down to write the account of his expedition to Erebor with Thorin and Company (known to us as *The Hobbit*).

GIMLI THE DWARF

Gimli is the chosen Dwarves representative in the Company of the Ring. Devoted to Galadriel and a close friend of Legolas, he fights valiantly in a number of battles.

Other Collections

SAM GAMGEE

CODE: 5028
ISSUED: January 1992
DESIGNER: JW **MODELLER:** RG
SIZE: 3" x 2" x 3"
ISSUE PRICE: £14.95

Frodo's loyal and devoted servant, who inherits Bag End when Frodo goes 'over Sea', marries Rose Cotton and has thirteen children. He is also elected Mayor of the Shire, where most Hobbits live.

ARAGORN (STRIDER) ▶

A bold warrior, friend of Gandalf and, after thirteen years of intermittent searching, the capturer of Gollum. Strider was his name before the War of the Ring.

CODE: 5029
ISSUED: January 1992
DESIGNER: JW **MODELLER:** AS
SIZE: 3" x 2¹⁄₂" x 4"
ISSUE PRICE: £14.95

◀ AN ORC

CODE: 5030
ISSUED: January 1992
DESIGNER: JW **MODELLER:** RG
SIZE: 3¹⁄₂" x 2" x 4¹⁄₄"
ISSUE PRICE: £17.95

Orcs are an evil race who wear foul, coarse clothing and heavy shoes. There are many different tribes who hate each other as much as they hate everything else. Scheduled for retirement: 31st December 1994

LEGOLAS THE ELF

CODE: 5031
ISSUED: January 1992
DESIGNER: JW MODELLER: AS
SIZE: 2¹/₂" x 2¹/₂" x 3¹/₄"
ISSUE PRICE: £17.95

Legolas represents the Elves as one of the Companions of the Ring. His name means 'green leaf' and he is a lifelong friend of Gimli the Dwarf.

THE MIRROR OF GAL-ADRIEL ▼

When filled with water, the Mirror of Galadriel gives glimpses of scenes far away in time or space.

CODE: 5032
ISSUED: January 1992
DESIGNER: JW MODELLER: RG
SIZE: 3" x 2¹/₄" x 4"
ISSUE PRICE: £17.95

CODE: 5033
ISSUED: January 1992
DESIGNER: JW MODELLER: AS (RG)
SIZE: 2¹/₄" x 3" x 5"
ISSUE PRICE: £25.75

SARUMAN

Ambitious and manipulative, Saruman brings on his own destruction during the War of the Ring by sending an Orc band against the Fellowship of the Ring. Eventually he is cast out of the Shire by Frodo and slain. Scheduled for retirement: 31st December 1994

other collections

◄ THE BALROG

CODE: 5034
ISSUED: January 1992
DESIGNER: JW MODELLER: RG
SIZE: 3³/₄" x 3¹/₄" x 6¹/₄"
ISSUE PRICE: £39.95

Balrogs are spirits of fire and carry whips of flame, and this particular Balrog is a survivor of the Great Battle who fled underground, emerging later to rule Orcs and Trolls by terror. Gandalf finally destroys him, but only after a ten-day battle.

GANDALF AND SHADOWFAX ►

CODE: 5035
ISSUED: January 1992
DESIGNER: JW MODELLER: ML
SIZE: 4³/₄" x 2¹/₂" x 5¹/₂"
ISSUE PRICE: £39.95

Shadowfax is given to Gandalf by King Theodon, and the horse bears the Wizard faithfully throughout the War of the Ring, without bridle or saddle. Shadowfax is extremely strong and swift; he got his name because his coat is silver-grey.

CODE: 5036
ISSUED: January 1992
DESIGNER: JW MODELLER: AS
SIZE: 4¹/₂" x 3¹/₂" x 6"
ISSUE PRICE: £39.95

A BLACK RIDER

The Black Riders are the Nazgul, nine servants of Sauron, and so called because they ride swift black horses. Sauron sends them to the Shire to search for Frodo and the Ring. Although wounded, Frodo escapes from them, and their steeds are later destroyed in the Ford of Bruinen.

PIPPIN (PEREGRIN TOOK)

CODE: 5037
ISSUED: August 1992
DESIGNER: JW MODELLER: AS
SIZE: 2" x 2" x 3¹/₄"
ISSUE PRICE: £14.95

Peregrin Took — known universally as Pippin — is a Hobbit, a close friend of Frodo's in his youth who later slays a great troll in battle and becomes a King's messenger. Scheduled for retirement: 31st December 1994

MERRY (MERIADOC BRANDY-BUCK) ▼

Meriadoc Brandybuck is always called Merry. He and Pippin share much in common, including their size: they are the largest Hobbits in history — at least four and a half feet tall.
Scheduled for retirement: 31st December 1994

CODE: 5038
ISSUED: August 1992
DESIGNER: JW MODELLER: AS
SIZE: 3" x 2" x 3"
ISSUE PRICE: £14.95

CODE: 5039
ISSUED: August 1992
DESIGNER: JW MODELLER: RG
SIZE: 2¹/₄" x 2¹/₄" x 4"
ISSUE PRICE: £14.95

BOROMIR

Affected by the spell of the Ring, Boromir tries to kill Frodo. He immediately repents and later dies defending Merry and Pippin from Orc raiders. After a proper funeral, his body is set afloat on the river Anguin. Scheduled for retirement: 31st December 1994

TREEBEARD (FANGORN) ▼

The guardian of Fangorn Forest, Treebeard is an Ent, and the oldest living being in Middle-earth. As his name so aptly suggests, he is bearded and resembles an evergreen tree! Scheduled for retirement: 31st December 1994.

CODE: 5040
ISSUED: August 1992
DESIGNER: JW MODELLER: RG
SIZE: 2³/₄" x 2¹/₄" x 5"
ISSUE PRICE: £25.75

THE ARTHURIAN LEGEND

It was soon apparent after the initial launch of *Myth and Magic* that a range of figurines based on the Arthurian legend would appeal to collectors. The first six were released in January 1990 and the collection is currently fourteen strong — all the designs are by Sharon Riley (but see 3203 and 3209), and modelling is primarily the work of Mark Locker. (It was originally intended that Mark would do all the *Fantasy and Legend* work.) All the figurines were inspired by Sharon's reading, and viewing, of material based on the subject; her sources included Mallory's *Le Morte d'Arthur*, John Boorman's film *Excalibur* and Marion Bradley's 1982 work *The Mists of Avalon*.

The Tudor Mint say that although the series continues to be popular, it is difficult to envisage further additions as the main characters and scenes from the Arthurian legend which are known to the general public have been covered. As Graham Hughes comments: "There are numerous other knights of the Round Table, certainly, but who can name them?"

Le Morte D'Arthur is also part of *The Arthurian Legend* but is listed in the section on Larger Studies.

Typical base marking: FANTASY & LEGEND KING ARTHUR BY Mark Locker WAPW © U.K. (plus logo of a jousting knight on horseback).

MERLIN

In case anyone doesn't know, Merlin is the magician around whom much of the Arthurian tales revolve. Here he is seen casting a spell.

CODE: 3200
ISSUED: January 1990
DESIGNER: SR MODELLER: ML
SIZE: 2" x 1" x 3"
ISSUE PRICE: £10.95

INTO MERLIN'S CARE

Part of the contract between Uther Pendragon and Merlin is that Merlin should be given the child of the union between Uther and Igraine. Here the infant Arthur is passed into Merlin's care. Mould 1 had much thinner drapes on the crib than Mould 2.

CODE: 3201
ISSUED: January 1990
RETIRED: December 1993
DESIGNER: SR MODELLER: ML
SIZE: 2 1/2" x 2 1/2" x 3 1/4"
ISSUE PRICE: £14.95

Other Collections

EXCALIBUR

he study depicts the sword being pulled from the stone, which is most people's impression of Excalibur. However, in Mallory's version of the Arthurian tale, Excalibur is *not* the Sword in the Stone but the sword loaned to Arthur by the Lady of the Lake. Collectors don't seem to mind this spot of artistic license and the study is very popular. Originally the base was hollow (Mould 1), but at some stage it was filled to make it more solid (Mould 2). Although credited to Mark Locker, this study is actually the work of Roger Gibbons.

CODE: 3202
ISSUED: January 1990
DESIGNER: SR MODELLER: ML (RG)
SIZE: 1¹/₂" x 1¹/₂" x 2¹/₂"
ISSUE PRICE: £10.95

CAMELOT

Camelot was also the name of the town where Arthur's court was situated, but the name is primarily associated with his castle, as this study reflects. Mould 1 of the study was 'hollow', in that the two central turrets arose from a courtyard. In Mould 2 the courtyard was filled in. This is the only study in the whole collection designed by Ruth Calderbank, who is no longer with The Tudor Mint.

CODE: 3203
ISSUED: January 1990
DESIGNER: Ruth Calderbank
MODELLER: ML
SIZE: 2¹/₂" x 2¹/₂" x 2¹/₄"
ISSUE PRICE: £14.95

CODE: 3204
ISSUED: January 1990
DESIGNER: SR MODELLER: ML (RG)
SIZE: 1³/₄" x 2" x 3¹/₂"
ISSUE PRICE: £10.95

KING ARTHUR

The 6th-century king of the Britons and leader of the knights of the Round Table who led Celtic resistance against the Saxons. His figure is the core of the romantic legend which inspire the collection. Despite the nameplate credit, this too is the work of Roger Gibbons, and the study can sometimes be found with a cubic crystal.

Other Collections

QUEEN GUINEVERE ▶

CODE: 3205
ISSUED: January 1990
DESIGNER: SR MODELLER: ML
SIZE: 2¹/₄" x 1¹/₂" x 2³/₄"
ISSUE PRICE: £10.95

Queen Guinevere, wife of King Arthur and lover of Lancelot. The crystal settings proved awkward in early issues, and a slight restyling took place so that more room was allowed to position them. The change is so slight that it does not constitute a remoulding.

CODE: 3206
ISSUED: August 1990
RETIRED: December 1993
DESIGNER: SR MODELLER: AS
SIZE: 2¹/₄" x 2" x 3"
ISSUE PRICE: £10.95

◀ SIR PERCIVAL AND THE GRAIL

Sir Percival was the only one of Arthur's knights pure enough to succeed in the quest for the Holy Grail. In the study he is seen receiving it.

MORGAN LE FEY

Morgan Le Fey — half-sister to Arthur and mother of his child, Mordred. She is seen in this study on the shores of Lake Avalon. Although she is given a variety of names in the Arthurian tales, she is more usually called Morgan le Fay, as in fairy, rather than Fey, as in whimsy.

CODE: 3207
ISSUED: August 1990
DESIGNER: SR MODELLER: ML
SIZE: 3¹/₄" x 2" x 3¹/₄"
ISSUE PRICE: £14.95

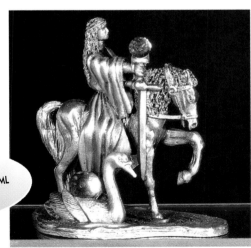

SIR LANCELOT ▶

T he greatest and most famous of the knights of the Round Table, and the paramour of Queen Guinevere. Mould 2 of the study adds more of a rim around the crystal, whilst Mould 3 (remodelling by Roger Gibbons) added a more textured cloak and a riveted helmet.

CODE: 3208
ISSUED: August 1990
DESIGNER: SR MODELLER: ML
SIZE: 2" x 1" x 3$^{1}/_{4}$"
ISSUE PRICE: £14.95

CODE: 3209
ISSUED: January 1992
DESIGNER: SR/M MODELLER: AS
SIZE: 2$^{3}/_{4}$" x 2$^{1}/_{4}$" x 3"
ISSUE PRICE: £18.50

THE VIGIL OF SIR GALAHAD

T he design for The Vigil of Sir Galahad came initially from Sonz Griffiths-Glover, who earned second prize in the 'Design a Study' competition in the Methtintdour Times (issue 4), and was redrawn by Sharon Riley. Roger Gibbons restyled the setting of the crystal for Mould 2 of the study in May 1994, as in Mould 1 it was occasionally knocked off.

SIR MORDRED

T he knight of the Round Table who rebelled and killed his uncle-father, King Arthur. This is the only study in the

CODE: 3210
ISSUED: January 1992
DESIGNER: SR MODELLER: RG
SIZE: 2" x 1$^{1}/_{2}$" x 3$^{1}/_{2}$"
ISSUE PRICE: £13.95

Arthurian Legend series officially credited to Roger Gibbons, though he also sculpted Excalibur and King Arthur.

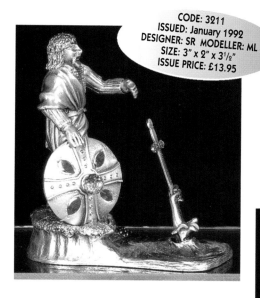

CODE: 3211
ISSUED: January 1992
DESIGNER: SR MODELLER: ML
SIZE: 3" x 2" x 3½"
ISSUE PRICE: £13.95

RETURN OF EXCALIBUR

In Mould 1, the back of the shield was plain; however, in response to collectors' comments, this was altered in October 1992 to a 'wooden' texture with rivetted edges and handles (Mould 2), giving the study a whole new realism. Mould 3 was released in April 1994 with improved crystal settings. The study depicts Sir Bedevere returning Excalibur to the Lady of the Lake.

CODE: 3212
ISSUED: August 1993
DESIGNER: SR MODELLER: AS
SIZE: 3" x 1¾" x 3¾"
ISSUE PRICE: £14.95

SIR GAWAIN ▶

Sir Gawain is seen here on his quest for The Green Knight. In Mould 1 Gawain has a shorter cloak which does not touch the base, whereas in Mould 2 it does.

CODE: 3213
ISSUED: August 1993
DESIGNER: SR MODELLER: ML
SIZE: 3½" x 2½" x 2¾"
ISSUE PRICE: £19.95

KING ARTHUR AND SIR BEDEVERE

The study depicts Arthur in death, accompanied by Sir Bedevere, who has survived the final battle.

DARK *SECRETS*

Dark Secrets were launched in January 1994. The Tudor Mint do not class them as *Myth and Magic* as they wish to keep the more macabre subject matter of the collection separate from the relatively innocuous world of wizards, unicorns, dragons and flying horses. Nevertheless it was the success of one *Myth and Magic* study in particular, The Keeper of the Skulls, which encouraged them to develop in depth the themes of skulls, demons and skeletons.

The collection of *Dark Secrets* is divided into three 'chambers' — The Chamber of the Skulls and The Chamber of the Demons were the original pair and The Chamber of Skeletons followed six months later in July 1994. Each 'chamber' consists of eight studies (seven standard-sized and one larger) plus the separate larger study which gives the collection its name — *Dark Secrets*.

The Tudor Mint offer a choice of a free talisman to collectors who return four tokens to them (there is one token in the box with every piece, except *Dark Secrets* itself — four 'skull tokens' for a Skull Talisman, four 'demon tokens' for a Demon Talisman and four 'skeleton tokens' for a Skeleton Talisman.

Although some Dark Secrets studies have mould variations, these are not reflected in the Secondary Market Price Guide (on pages 132-135) as their market values are not yet discernible.

Typical base marking: DARK SECRETS - THE ICE DEMON BY S.P. Darnley 6211 WAPW © U.K.

CODE: 6201
ISSUED: January 1994
DESIGNER: JW MODELLER: AS
SIZE: 5" x 3 1/2" x 3 1/2"
ISSUE PRICE: £49.95

DARK SECRETS

The goblin on this study also appears on The Chamber of the Skulls. The study depicts goblins being freed by the good wizard. A soldering variation exists in which the little demon at the front left of the portal faces the wrong way (i.e. to the left instead of peering into the doorway).

CODE: 6202
ISSUED: January 1994
DESIGNER: HC MODELLER: RG
SIZE: 2 1/2" x 2 1/4" x 3 1/2"
ISSUE PRICE: £17.75

THE GUARDIAN OF THE SKULLS ▶

Designer Helen Coventry was pleased with the outcome of this study; "The oafy, huge fat thing was a pleasure to design," she says. It's also one of Roger Gibbons' favourites, and collectors, too, seem to like it: The Guardian of the Skulls is one of the best selling pieces of 1994.

Other Collections

THE SKULL GATEWAY ▶

CODE: 6203
ISSUED: January 1994
DESIGNER: SR MODELLER: ML
SIZE: 2 ¾" x 3" x 3 ¼"
ISSUE PRICE: £19.95

In Mould 1 of this study the two turrets had a tendency to pull at the moulds; a smoothing 'moss' was added to Mould 2. Unspeakable events happen within the gateway; only the bravest will enter.

THE TORTURED SKULL ▼

Just about as tortured as a skull can get, this is nevertheless one of Mark Locker's favourite studies — "anatomically very good," he says. In Mould 1 the eye sockets are smaller; the two settings were considered inadequate and were soon redesigned for Mould 2. Another big seller.

CODE: 6204
ISSUED: January 1994
DESIGNER: SR MODELLER: ML
SIZE: 2 ¾" x 2 ½" x 2 ¾"
ISSUE PRICE: £19.95

THE SERPENTS OF THE SKULLS ▶

The study depicts a number of snakes writhing around a pile of decaying skulls. Lovely. (Tudor Mint's *Dark Secrets* brochure erroneously refers to just one - The Serpent of the Skulls — but the nameplate is correctly in the plural.)

CODE: 6205
ISSUED: January 1994
DESIGNER: JW MODELLER: SD
SIZE: 2 ¼" x 2 ¼" x 2 ¾"
ISSUE PRICE: £19.95

THE ALTAR OF THE SKULLS

In this study the skulls ward off those who would abuse the altar.

CODE: 6206
ISSUED: January 1994
DESIGNER: JW MODELLER: ML
SIZE: 2 ½" x 2 ¼" x 2 ¾"
ISSUE PRICE: £14.95

THE SKULL MASTER

Mould 1 has smaller gaps between the skull and the cape; these were widened in Mould 2. The study is now cast in two halves, whereas originally it was one whole piece.

CODE: 6207
ISSUED: January 1994
DESIGNER: JW MODELLER: RG
SIZE: 2 3/4" x 2" x 3 1/4"
ISSUE PRICE: £19.95

THE VAMPIRE OF THE SKULLS

A vampire is seen here stealing the last rays of life from the atrophied remains.

CODE: 6208
ISSUED: January 1994
DESIGNER: JW MODELLER: AS
SIZE: 2 3/4" X 2 1/2" X 2 3/4"
ISSUE PRICE: £14.95

THE CHAMBER OF THE SKULLS

The Chamber of the Skulls

Look carefully at the book on the altar: therein lies the mysterious name 'Jack' (surname Slocombe, son of Anthony). It was clear soon into production that the wizard's right arm and neck were too thin, and they were both thickened up for Mould 2.

CODE: 6209
ISSUED: January 1994
DESIGNER: JW MODELLER: AS
SIZE: 5" x 3 1/2" x 5"
ISSUE PRICE: £59.95

Other Collections

THE GUARDIAN OF THE DEMONS

CODE: 6210
ISSUED: January 1994
DESIGNER: HC MODELLER: ML
SIZE: 2 ½" x 2 ¾" x 3"
ISSUE PRICE: £17.75

Helen Coventry's original design featured a demon rather than a guardian, but whatever the figure he is clearly an imposing one. Able to see the future (note the tarot cards and crystal ball), the guardian warns the 'unready' with the skull, in his right hand.

THE ICE DEMON

CODE: 6211
ISSUED: January 1994
DESIGNER: SR MODELLER: SD
SIZE: 2 ¾" x 2" x 3 ¼"
ISSUE PRICE: £14.95

The 'ice crystals' at the front of the study caused a few problems and were quickly reduced in size and made integral to the base (Mould 2).

THE DEMON OF THE PIT ▶

Helen Coventry didn't have time to finish her design for The Demon of the Pit before taking a holiday. On her return she found that the model was done, sculpted to her incomplete design! You'd never know from looking at the released study and this is another popular seller. A small number of models with the archway soldered on the wrong way round are believed to exist.

CODE: 6212
ISSUED: January 1994
DESIGNER: HC MODELLER: SD
SIZE: 3" x 2" x 2 ¾"
ISSUE PRICE: £14.95

CODE: 6213
ISSUED: January 1994
DESIGNER: HC MODELLER: ML
SIZE: 3" x 2 ½" x 3"
ISSUE PRICE: £14.95

◀ THE DEMON OF THE NIGHT

Here the demon is seen stalking around a forbidding graveyard.

THE DEMON OF THE CATACOMBS

CODE: 6214
ISSUED: January 1994
DESIGNER: SR MODELLER: RG
SIZE: 3 ¼" x 2" x 3 ½"
ISSUE PRICE: £14.95

According to the nameplate, 'The Demon of the Catacombs'; according to Sharon Riley, "a hideous swamp-sort-of-thing." Both descriptions are accurate.

CODE: 6215
ISSUED: January 1994
DESIGNER: HC MODELLER: ML
SIZE: 3" x 1 ¾" x 3 ¼"
ISSUE PRICE: £14.95

THE DEMON SLAYER ▶

Helen Coventry gave this study a working title — 'The Lacerator' — and it's easy to see why.

CODE: 6216
ISSUED: January 1994
DESIGNER: HC MODELLER: SD
SIZE: 2 ¾" x 2 ¼" x 3 ¼"
ISSUE PRICE: 14.95

THE DEMON JAILER ▲

The jailer is seen stopping the trap door with his foot, with rather unpleasant consequences for the would-be escapees beneath.

CODE: 6217
ISSUED: January 1994
DESIGNER: JW MODELLER: AS
SIZE: 5" x 3 ½" x 4 ½"
ISSUE PRICE: £59.95

THE CHAMBER OF THE DEMONS

Roger Gibbons produced a slightly modified mount for the crystal in April 1994, although the change was minor.

The Chamber of the Demons

THE GUARDIAN OF THE SKELETONS

Although Jessica Watson designed all the studies in the third *Dark Secrets* set, the Chamber of the Skeletons includes work by all four model makers. This one is by Roger Gibbons. The crown gives the guardian an arrogant as well as authoritative air.

CODE: 6218
ISSUED: July 1994
DESIGNER: JW MODELLER: RG
SIZE: 2 3/4" x 2 3/4" x 3 1/2"
ISSUE PRICE: £17.95

THE VIGIL OF THE SKELETON ▶

CODE: 6219
ISSUED: July 1994
DESIGNER: JW MODELLER: RG
SIZE: 2 1/4" x 2 1/4" x 3 1/2"
ISSUE PRICE: £14.95

What, one has to ask, was he waiting for . . . for so long? There are clues to be found on the study that might lead to a fascinating storyline; the bat, for example, and the crystal itself. Or is it a female who has kept the vigil? It's hard to tell the difference with skeletons.

CODE: 6220
ISSUED: July 1994
DESIGNER: JW MODELLER: RG
SIZE: 3 1/4" x 2 1/4" x 3 1/4"
ISSUE PRICE: £17.95

THE FORGOTTEN SKELETON

. . . a condition not unreminiscent of that brought on by waiting for a number 85 bus on Kingston Hill. (Here speaks the voice of someone who has experienced this nightmarish torture first hand!)

THE PRISONERS OF THE SWORD

The crystal is cleverly incorporated into the study as part of the ball and chain holding down one of the prisoners. There is a definite sense of finality about their incarceration; these skeletons will clearly be there forever.

CODE: 6221
ISSUED: July 1994
DESIGNER: JW MODELLER: AS
SIZE: 3 ¼" x 2 ¼" x 3 ¼"
ISSUE PRICE: £17.95

▼ THE EXECUTIONER

A deceptively simple study, yet the skeletal figure creates a hauntingly sinister impression.

CODE: 6222
ISSUED: July 1994
DESIGNER: JW MODELLER: ML
SIZE: 3 ¼" x 2 ¼" x 3 ½"
ISSUE PRICE: £17.95

CODE: 6223
ISSUED: July 1994
DESIGNER: JW MODELLER: AS
SIZE: 3 ¼" x 2 ¼" x 3 ½"
ISSUE PRICE: £14.95

THE FINDER OF THE TREASURE

The unfortunate 'finder' appears never to have benefited from his good fortune; he has been attacked in some way at the very zenith of his quest . . . Although this study survived the rigours of the 'drop test', it caused a few problems in The Tudor Mint's packing department. The crystal was prone to damage as it was placed in the polystyrene packaging, and so a slight modification was made (prior to release).

Other Collections

CODE: 6224
ISSUED: July 1994
DESIGNER: JW MODELLER: SD
SIZE: 2 ½" x 2 ¼" x 3 ½"
ISSUE PRICE: £17.95

THE SKELETON WARRIOR

Reminiscent of one of the small army of skeleton warriors brought to life by animator Ray Harryhausen in 1963 for the film *Jason and the Argonauts* (though there is no conscious connection in the design of this study). The difference is that here the warrior sits astride a dragon skeleton. More than thirty years later, the image of a fleshless fighter still has a sinister appeal.

CODE: 6225
ISSUED: July 1994
DESIGNER: JW MODELLER: AS
SIZE: 5" x 3 ½" x 5 ¾"
ISSUE PRICE: £59.95

THE CHAMBER OF THE SKELETONS

Three skeletons are chained around the crystal, which is clearly precious to them, whilst an army of skeletons surround the base of the study as a further line of protection. This study is pictured here without its wooden plinth.

Rare and Unreleased Studies

Hidden in a cupboard at The Tudor Mint are all sorts of fascinating things — a veritable Aladdin's cave that would make the well-healed *Myth and Magic* collector drool uncontrollably. Some will be familiar (though highly sought after), whilst others have barely seen the light of day before.

THE DRAGON OF THE MOUNTAINS

The Dragon of the Mountains, designed by Jessica Watson and sculpted by Mark Locker, was never released for the simple reason that Graham Hughes just didn't like the completed model. For the record, it measures 2" x 2" x 3" and has the base marking: THE DRAGON OF THE MOUNTAIN BY Mark Locker WAPW © U.K.

DRAGON OF THE CLOUDS PROTOTYPE ▼

The difference between a prototype and the released study are sometimes minimal, but with The Dragon of the Clouds the changes are clear for all to see. The prototype is taller and has shorter wings, with the dragon supported only by its tail on a blanket of clouds. In the released version, the dragon is sitting on the clouds, its feet are firmly attached to the base and the larger wings curve (bat-like) in a 180 degree arc. The reasons for the changes are apparent, and the prototype looks unlikely to have survived the 'drop test', let alone the rigours of delivery from The Tudor Mint to stores worldwide.

PAINTED STUDIES

Between 1990 and 1992 The Tudor Mint produced hand-painted versions of nine of the larger studies. They did not prove particularly popular with collectors — the general census of opinion being that they were not in keeping with the rest of the collection — and they were phased out in mid-1992. Consequently they have now developing a rarity value and currently fetch £150-200 on the secondary market. Pictured here is The Sorceror's Apprentice in its painted version.

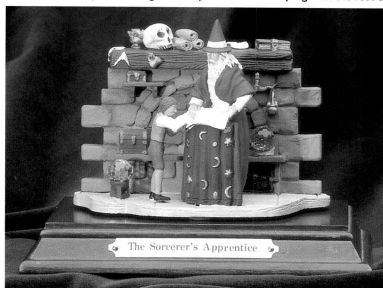

The Sorcerer's Apprentice

UNRELEASED PAINTED STUDIES

Painted versions of two standard-sized studies, The Incantation and The Siren, were also produced, but only as test samples. They were never released commercially, and these two extreme rarities belong to The Tudor Mint.

Rare and Unreleased

The Sorcerer's Apprentice

The Sorcerer's Apprentice

ANOTHER BRICK IN THE WALL

Initial critical appreciation of a new study counts for a great deal, and with *Myth and Magic* this often comes from trade shows, where they are first seen by (you guessed) the trade. In the case of The Sorceror's Apprentice, seen here, it had to do with the walls; too straight and symmetrical on the original — a bit more irregularity needed. So back at The Mint, a few extra bricks were inserted and before you can say *Fantasia*, hey presto, you have a much improved study. The Dawn of the Dragon was another example; early comments from stockists resulted in an immediate remodelling to give the study an injection of life. Sometimes two heads are definitely better than one.

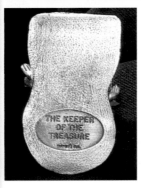

AUTOGRAPH HUNTERS NEED NOT APPLY

It has to be confessed that the issue The Keeper of the Treasure was a bit of a 'rushed job.' Problems had arisen with The Evil of Greed, which necessitated its withdrawal from the collection, and a replacement was needed quickly. In the midst of all the hoopla, a nameplate was produced minus a very obvious regular feature . . . the sculptor's signature! The exact number of studies issued without credit to Roger Gibbons is known to be in the region of 200. The error was then rectified.

WINGS AIN'T WOT THEY USED TO BE

The Dragon of the Underworld, The Armoured Dragon, The Oriental Dragon . . . there's no doubt about it, wings can be difficult! Shown here is the original Dragon of the Underworld, with its wings apart. Unfortunately they kept breaking in production, and now they are well and truly joined together.

HUBBLE BUBBLE, LOADS OF TROUBLE!

The story of The Cauldron of Light is a bit of an epic and can be found in full in the listing of current studies. But as Kojak growled rather unmusically once, 'a picture paints a thousand words,' and from this comparison of three models you can see just how altered the wizard and his cauldron have been. Sometimes these changes can be just as revealing to the sculptors themselves, whose records are very occasionally not quite up-to-scratch. (The same can be said of Kojak's.)

WHAT GOES UP . . .

Three examples of the inevitability of gravity. The Winged Serpent initially had greater flying aspirations (bottom picture), and the versions illustrated here show how the wings were lowered for Mould 2. Breakage during transit ensured a less lofty perch. The Giant Sorceror (below), meanwhile, was at first proud to shine forth a crystal in his raised hand. Pride, as we all know, comes before a fall, and to demonstrate that size isn't everything, he was soon reduced to holding the crystal more respectfully. Finally, The Infernal Demon (below right) may have started with raised expectations, but his right forearm tended to damage moulds. It was lowered — out of arms way, as it were.

Two Mould 2 versions with slightly different tales

Mould 1

YOU NEED HANDS

bviously a lesson to be learned here; if you're going to ride a dragon, make up your mind which hand you're going to hold the crystal in. Three versions of The Dragon Rider prove the point. Initially the rider held the crystal in his right hand (middle), but then changed it to the left hand. In the process, the use of reins appears optional! Of the two 'left-hand' versions pictured here, one has a global and the other a conical crystal.

A CRYSTAL CLEAR DIFFERENCE

ere we have two examples of a discontinued study — The Water Wizard. One has a global crystal and one has a conical crystal. Apart from this obvious difference they are identical. Yet such is the rarity value of the conical version that it can fetch up to three times the price of its 'global' counterpart on the secondary market.

DESIGN A MODEL WINNERS

The 1992 Extravaganza saw the first 'Design a Model' competition. Designs were drawn by collectors actually on the day, and a winner, Gary Jones, selected by The Tudor Mint's three designers. Gary's design, 'Zeus', was then redrawn by Sharon Riley and modelled by Roger Gibbons (part of the prize is to select the model maker of your choice to sculpt your study). Only two casts were made; one for Gary and the other for The Tudor Mint's archive. A similar competition was held at the 1993 Extravaganza, and the winner that year was Karen Burrows for design entitled 'Fight for Freedom'. Karen chose Mark Locker as her sculptor. In both instances, the winner's model had a special brass nameplate, whereas the Tudor Mint's copy has a regular nameplate.

ZEUS

DESIGNER: SR / Gary Jones
MODELLER: RG
SIZE: 4 ¹/₂" x 2 ¹/₂" x 3 ¹/₂"
MARKINGS: ZEUS BY Roger Gibbons EXCLUSIVE
SCULPTURE MYTH AND MAGIC EXTRAVAGANZA
DESIGN A MODEL WINNER GARY JONES 11th
October 1992 WAPW © U.K.

FIGHT FOR FREEDOM

DESIGNER: JW / Karen Burrows
MODELLER: ML
SIZE: 4 ¹/₂" x 2 ¹/₂" x 3 ¹/₂"
MARKINGS: FIGHT FOR FREEDOM BY
Mark Locker EXCLUSIVE SCULPTURE
MYTH AND MAGIC EXTRAVAGANZA
DESIGN A MODEL WINNER KAREN
BURROWS 5th October 1993
WAPW © U.K.

Jessica Watson says that she modified Karen's design very little and the final modelled study is exactly how she had drawn it.

Miscellaneous and Memorabilia

This section lists miscellaneous items that do not fit into any other category — chess sets, paper knives, miniatures, Crystal Keepers and dinosaurs — and memorabilia such as plates, books, leaflets and ephemera associated with *Myth and Magic*.

CHESS SETS

FANTASY CHESS SET

The idea of a chess set was mooted long before this set, designed and sculpted by freelance artist John Pickering, was released in 1992. It was originally called the 'Myth and Magic' chess set but is now referred to as the 'Fantasy' set. As Allan Frost explains: "The set was withdrawn as it didn't really fit in with the atmosphere engendered by the rest of the *Myth and Magic* range." The Fantasy Chess Set was supplied with a wooden board, and although retired as a set, the individual pieces are still currently available.

CODE: 4305
ISSUED: August 1992
RETIRED: December 1994
DESIGNER: JP MODELLER: JP
ISSUE PRICE: £275

TUDOR MINT CHESS SET

The Fantasy Chess Set was replaced by a new set created internally at The Tudor Mint: Sharon Riley designed the pieces and they were modelled jointly by Roger Gibbons, Mark Locker and Anthony Slocombe. This chess set is available either complete (including a new black glass chess board) or as individual pieces: PAWN white (4306)/ black (4307); CASTLE white (4308)/ black (4309); KNIGHT white (4310)/ black (4311); BISHOP white (4312)/ black (4313); QUEEN white (4314)/ black (4315); KING white (4316)/ white (4317); BLACK GLASS BOARD (4321).

CODE: 4323
ISSUED: August 1993
DESIGNER: SR MODELLER: RG/ML/AS
ISSUE PRICE: £299

PAPER KNIVES / LETTER OPENERS

The 'Wizard' and 'Dragon' paper knives were released in August 1992 in response to collectors' requests and were based on the two main success areas of the collection.

They proved popular, and so a further four knives followed a year later, featuring new designs based upon best-selling studies. The reference codes, however, do not reflect the order of release; numerically the 'Wizard' and 'Dragon' knives appear last.

UNICORN PAPER KNIFE

CODE: 3086
ISSUED: August 1993
DESIGNER: SR MODELLER: RG
LENGTH: 7³/₄"
MARKINGS: None
ISSUE PRICE: £13.95

CASTLE PAPER KNIFE

CODE: 3087
ISSUED: August 1993
DESIGNER: SR MODELLER: ML/RG
LENGTH: 8"
MARKINGS: None
ISSUE PRICE: £13.95
CURRENT VALUE: (Mould1) £20;
(Mould 2) List Price

Mark Locker made the Mould 1 'Castle'; it was much flatter and wider that the current Mould 2 version, which is the work of Roger Gibbons.

SKULLS PAPER KNIFE

CODE: 3088
ISSUED: August 1993
DESIGNER: SR MODELLER: RG
LENGTH: 8"
MARKINGS: None
ISSUE PRICE: £13.95

PEGASUS PAPER KNIFE

CODE: 3089
ISSUED: August 1993
DESIGNER: SR MODELLER: RG
LENGTH: 8"
MARKINGS: None
ISSUE PRICE: £13.95

WIZARD PAPER KNIFE

CODE: 3090
ISSUED: August 1992
DESIGNER: SR MODELLER: AS
LENGTH: 8"
MARKINGS: None
ISSUE PRICE: £13.65
CURRENT VALUE: (Mould 1) £15;
(Mould 2) List Price

Originally the crystal setting was much smaller (Mould 1); Anthony Slocombe redesigned the mount for Mould 2.

DRAGON PAPER KNIFE

CODE: 3091
ISSUED: August 1992
DESIGNER: SR MODELLER: RG
LENGTH: 7³/₄"
MARKINGS: None
ISSUE PRICE: £13.65
CURRENT VALUE: (Mould 1) £30;
(Mould 2) List Price

The Mould 1 'Dragon' was slightly too thick for its packaging material, and had to be redesigned very soon after issue.

MINIATURES

Amongst other things, W.A.P. Watson Limited have long been an established manufacturer of souvenirs, and miniature versions of standard-sized *Myth and Magic* studies were created primarily to interest the tourist market. The first twelve were issued in the summer of 1989 — at the same time as some of their standard-sized equivalents — and there have been regular releases ever since, in batches ranging from eighteen to six. Only one of the Miniatures is not based on a standard-sized equivalent — The Castle of Souls.

Twenty-four Miniatures have so far been retired, with six more due to retire at the end of 1994. One or two are now fetching appreciable sums on the secondary market and others are expected to create growing interest in the future. Some Miniatures were issued with cubic crystals and these now fetch a premium.

The Incantation

Code: 3500
Issued: July 1989
Retired: December 1991
Issue Price: £4.95

The White Witch

Code: 3505
Issued: July 1989
Retired: December 1991
Issue Price: £4.95

The Book of Spells

Code: 3501
Issued: July 1989
Issue Price: £4.95

The Master Wizard

Code: 3506
Issued: July 1989
Issue Price: £4.95

The Enchanted Castle

Code: 3502
Retired: December 1993
Issued: July 1989
Issue Price: £4.95

The Guardian Dragon

Code: 3507
Issued: July 1989
Issue Price: £4.95

The Cauldron of Light

Code: 3503
Issued: July 1989
Issue Price: £4.95

The Unicorn

Code: 3508
Issued: July 1989
Issue Price: £4.95

The Winged Serpent

Code: 3504
Issued: July 1989
Issue Price: £4.95

Pegasus

Code: 3509
Issued: July 1989
Issue Price: £4.95

Miscellaneous

The Castle of Dreams

Code: 3510
Issued: July 1989
Retired: December 1993
Issue Price: £4.95

The original (Mould 1) was completely redesigned as it was very similar to a model produced by another company. Very few originals were made and some can be found without a baseplate. The restyled version (Mould 2) is by far the more common of the two. Both designs exist only as a miniature; they have no standard-sized equivalents.

The Light of Knowledge

Code: 3511
Issued: July 1989
Retired: December 1991
Issue Price: £4.95

The Siren

Code: 3512
Issued: January 1990
Retired: January 1991
Issue Price: £4.95

The Crystal Queen

Code: 3513
Issued: January 1990
Retired: December 1992
Issue Price: £5.15

The Astronomer

Code: 3514
Issued: January 1990
Retired: January 1991
Issue Price: £5.15

The Alchemist

Code: 3515
Issued: January 1990
Retired: January 1991
Issue Price: £5.15

The Minotaur

Code: 3516
Issued: January 1990
Retired: December 1991
Issue Price: £5.15

The Grim Reaper

Code: 3517
Issued: January 1990
Issue Price: £5.15

The Castle of Souls

Code: 3518
Issued: January 1990
Retired: December 1993
Issue Price: £5.15

The Dragon Gateway

Code: 3519
Issued: January 1990
Issue Price: £5.15

The Dragon Rider

Code: 3520
Issued: January 1990
Retired: January 1991
Issue Price: £5.15

The Giant Sorceror

Code: 3526
Issued: January 1990
Retired: December 1991
Issue Price: £5.15

The Dragon's Kiss

Code: 3521
Issued: January 1990
Retired: December 1992
Issue Price: £5.15

The Wizard of Light

Scheduled for retirement: 31st December 1994.

Code: 3527
Issued: January 1990
Issue Price: £5.15

The Witch and Familiar

Code: 3522
Issued: January 1990
Retired: January 1991
Issue Price: £5.15

The Keeper of the Treasure

Code: 3528
Issued: January 1990
Retired: December 1992
Issue Price: £5.15

The Oriental Dragon

Code: 3523
Issued: January 1990
Retired: December 1993
Issue Price: £5.15

The Old Hag

Code: 3529
Issued: January 1990
Retired: January 1991
Issue Price: £5.15

The Reborn Dragon

Code: 3524
Issued: January 1990
Issue Price: £5.15

Mother Nature

Scheduled for retirement: 31st December 1994.

Code: 3530
Issued: January 1991
Issue Price: £5.55

The Fire Dragon

Scheduled for retirement: 31st December 1994.

Code: 3525
Issued: January 1990
Issue Price: £5.15

The Earth Wizard

Code: 3531
Issued: January 1991
Retired: December 1992
Issue Price: £5.55

Miscellaneous

The Fire Wizard

Scheduled for retirement: 31st December 1994.

Code: 3532
Issued: January 1991
Issue Price: £5.55

Excalibur

Code: 3538
Issued: January 1991
Retired: December 1993
Issue Price: £5.55

The Water Wizard

Code: 3533
Issued: January 1991
Retired: December 1992
Issue Price: £5.55

Camelot

Code: 3539
Issued: January 1991
Issue Price: £5.55

The Air Wizard

Code: 3534
Issued: January 1991
Retired: December 1992
Issue Price: £5.55

King Arthur

Code: 3540
Issued: January 1991
Issue Price: £5.55

The Dragon of the Lake

Scheduled for retirement: 31st December 1994.

Code: 3535
Issued: January 1991
Issue Price: £5.55

Queen Guinevere

Code: 3541
Issued: January 1991
Retired: December 1993
Issue Price: £5.55

The Dragon's Spell

Code: 3536
Issued: January 1991
Retired: December 1991
Issue Price: £5.55

Dragon of the Forest

Code: 3542
Issued: August 1992
Issue Price: £5.95

Merlin

Code: 3537
Issued: January 1991
Issue Price: £5.55

Dragon of the Moon

Code: 3543
Issued: August 1992
Issue Price: £5.95

Wizard of Winter

Code: 3544
Issued: August 1992
Issue Price: £5.95

The Return of Excalibur

Scheduled for retirement: 31st December 1994.

Code: 3550
Issued: January 1993
Issue Price: £6.25

Dragon of Wisdom

Code: 3545
Issued: August 1992
Issue Price: £5.95

Magical Encounter

Code: 3551
Issued: January 1993
Issue Price: £6.25

Dragon of the Sun

Code: 3546
Issued: August 1992
Issue Price: £5.95

Ice Dragon

Code: 3552
Issued: January 1993
Issue Price: £6.25

Dragon of the Clouds

Code: 3547
Issued: August 1992
Issue Price: £5.95

Sleepy Dragon

Code: 3553
Issued: January 1993
Issue Price: £6.25

Moon Wizard

Code: 3548
Issued: January 1993
Issue Price: £6.25

The Keeper of the Skulls

Code: 3554
Issued: January 1994
Issue Price: £6.35

Unicorn of Light

Code: 3549
Issued: January 1993
Issue Price: £6.25

The Dark Dragon

Code: 3555
Issued: January 1994
Issue Price: £6.35

The Protector of the Young

Code: 3556
Issued: January 1994
Issue Price: £6.35

The Unicorns of Freedom

Code: 3558
Issued: January 1994
Issue Price: £6.35

The Dragon of Light

Code: 3557
Issued: January 1994
Issue Price: £6.35

The Defender of the Crystal

Code: 3559
Issued: January 1994
Issue Price: £6.35

CRYSTAL KEEPERS

Following suggestions from collectors for something in which to display precious stones, The Tudor Mint commissioned freelance artist John Pickering to design four studies which would serve the purpose, and the Crystal Keepers were the result.

d. UNICORN AND DAMSEL
CODE: 4301
ISSUED: January 1992
RETIRED: December 1992
DESIGNER: JP MODELLER: RG
SIZE: 3 1/2" x 3" x 1 1/2"
ISSUE PRICE: £12.95
CURRENT VALUE: £75

b. SLEEPING WIZARD
CODE: 4303
ISSUED: January 1992
RETIRED: December 1992
DESIGNER: JP MODELLER: RG
SIZE: 3 1/4" x 3 1/4" x 1 1/4"
ISSUE PRICE: £12.95
CURRENT VALUE: £75

c. DRAGON AND WARRIOR
CODE: 4302
ISSUED: January 1992
RETIRED: December 1992
DESIGNER: JP MODELLER: RG
SIZE: 3 1/2" x 3 1/2" x 1 1/2"
ISSUE PRICE: £12.95
CURRENT VALUE: £75

a. FIRE WIZARD
CODE: 4304
ISSUED: January 1992
RETIRED: December 1992
DESIGNER: JP MODELLER: RG
SIZE: 3 1/4" x 3 1/4" x 1 3/4"
ISSUE PRICE: £12.95
CURRENT VALUE: £75

THE DINOSAUR COLLECTION

A collection of six pieces, released during the dinosaur mania which followed in the wake of Steven Spielberg's film 'Jurassic Park'. This project generated great excitement in The Tudor Mint's design studio, but unfortunately all three designers (Sharon, Jessica and Helen) wanted to work on the two most visually impressive pieces — Tyrannosaurus Rex and Stegosaurus. The problem was solved in a most democratic fashion, by pulling the names out of a hat. (As it turned out, Helen Coventry got T. Rex and Stegosaurus went to Jessica Watson.)

Typical base marking THE DINOSAUR COLLECTION BY THE TUDOR MINT   SPINOSAURUS BY ROGER GIBBONS 6006 WAPW © U.K.

The Dinosaur Collection is scheduled for retirement on 31st December 1994.

PTERANODON

CODE: 6001
ISSUED: August 1993
DESIGNER: SR MODELLER: ML
SIZE: 3 1/4" x 2" x 3 1/4"
ISSUE PRICE: £14.95

TRICERATOPS

CODE: 6002
ISSUED: August 1993
DESIGNER: HC MODELLER: AS
SIZE: 3 1/2" x 2 1/4" x 2 1/4"
ISSUE PRICE: £14.95

STEGOSAURUS ▶

CODE: 6003
ISSUED: August 1993
DESIGNER: JW MODELLER: AS
SIZE: 3 1/4" x 2 1/4" x 2 1/2"
ISSUE PRICE: £14.95

BRONTOSAURUS ▶

CODE: 6004
ISSUED: August 1993
DESIGNER: JW MODELLER: ML
SIZE: 3 $\frac{1}{4}$" x 2 $\frac{1}{2}$" x 3"
ISSUE PRICE: £14.95

◀ TYRANNOSAURUS REX

CODE: 6005
ISSUED: August 1993
DESIGNER: HC MODELLER: AS
SIZE: 3 $\frac{1}{4}$" x 2" x 3 $\frac{1}{2}$"
ISSUE PRICE: £14.95

SPINOSAURUS ▶

CODE: 6006
ISSUED: August 1993
DESIGNER: SR MODELLER: RG
SIZE: 3 $\frac{1}{4}$" x 2" x 3 $\frac{1}{2}$"
ISSUE PRICE: £14.95

Miscellaneous

MEMORABILIA

L isted here are various items associated with the *Myth and Magic* collection, including plates, books and promotional material.

COLLECTORS PLATES

A set of four fine bone china plates were issued in 1992, designed by Joy Mulholland and produced in Stoke-on-Trent. Each plate depicted a fantasy scene based upon a *Myth and Magic* study. Production problems galore included the company in Stoke-on-Trent ceasing to trade and artwork, although excellent in its own right, not transferring successfully into plate form. To top it all, when a new supplier had been found, not all the plates they produced were uniform in diameter and did not necessarily fit into the 7" plate holders purchased by customers. When all four plates were retired in December 1993, it was the end of what Graham Hughes describes as a "mini horror story." Well, every cloud has a silver lining, and the plates are already showing rapid secondary market interest. If you're lucky, you may still find the odd set in shops at List Price.

1. Meeting of Unicorns

Code: 4401
Issued: January 1992
Retired: December 1993
Issue Price: £15.95
Current Value: £50-100

2. Cauldron of Light

Code: 4402
Issued: January 1992
Retired: December 1993
Issue Price: £15.95
Current Value: £50-100

3. The Guardian Dragon

Code: 4403
Issued: January 1992
Retired: December 1993
Issue Price: £15.95
Current Value: £50-100

4. The Dragon's Nest

Code: 4404
Issued: January 1992
Retired: December 1993
Issue Price: £15.95
Current Value: £50-100

T-SHIRT
(white or emerald green)
Code: MM01
Available in Small, Medium, Extra Large
Issue Price: £6.95

SWEAT SHIRT
(grey or royal blue)
Code: MM02
Available in Small, Medium, Large, Extra Large
Issue Price: £12.95

BASEBALL CAP
(blue, maroon, navy, red)
Code: MM03
Issue Price: £2.95

COLLECTORS CLUB MUG
(blue)
Code: MM04
Issue Price: £1.95

SILVER-PLATED SPOON
Code: MM05
Issue Price: £2.50

ENAMELLED KEY FOB
Code: MM06
Issue Price: £1.95

WINDOW STICKERS
Code: MM07
Issue Price: £0.35

ENAMELLED BADGE
Code: MM08
Issue Price: £1.00

THE STRACYL OF UNITY
Code: MM09
Issued: 1991
Issue Price: £9.95

A fantasy novel by Allan Frost, Editor of the Collectors Club newsletter, with illustrations by Jessica Watson. The story is set in the mysterious land of Methtintdour and involves the quest for the four parts of the Stracyl of Unity following the murder of Uttar, the Theign Supreme. Allan, who is fond of an anagram, features numerous people from The Tudor Mint in the names of his characters. Note also this curiously familiar word 'stracyl'! Available in hardback only.

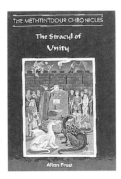

MYTH & MAGIC PEN
Code: MM10
Issue Price: £0.50

RECORD
"Sunshine in the Morning'
by Visions in Glass
(from Extravaganza 1991)
Issued: 1991
Code: MM11
Issue Price: £2.25

MAP OF METHTINTDOUR
Code: MM12
Issue Price: £1.00

DROUTS

Drouts are small coin-like discs issued by The Tudor Mint to commemorate certain special *Myth and Magic* events. So far, the following drouts have been issued (free of charge):

1991 Extravaganza
1992 Extravaganza
1993 Extravaganza
(1994 Extravaganza)
1991/2 Club Membership
1992/3 Club Membership
1993/4 Club Membership
1994/5 Club Membership

On the secondary market Extravaganza drouts are currently changing hands for £12 and Club Membership drouts for £5.

JEWELLERY

Were he alive today, W.A.P. Watson, the Birmingham jeweller whose initials are to be found on the baseplate of every *Myth and Magic* study, would be fascinated to know that an entirely new product created seventy-five years after he sold his business had turned full circle and generated . . . jewellery!

TRINKET BOXES

ISSUED: 1992/93
ISSUE PRICE: £11.95
CURRENT PRICE: £12.50

Wizard
Code: 1011

Dragon
Code: 1012

Unicorn
Code: 1013

Pegasus
Code: 1014

Dragon on Tower
Code: 1041

Wizard in Window
Code: 1042

Small Unicorn
Code: 1043

Dragon and Skulls
Code: 1044

Wizard and Damsels
Code: 1045

Unicorn
Code: 1046

Pegasus
Code: 1047

Pegasus and Girl
Code: 1048

PEWTER KEY CHAINS

ISSUED: 1992/3
ISSUE PRICE: £3.99
CURRENT PRICE: £4.25

Unicorn
Code: 1015

Pegasus
Code: 1016

Wizard's Head
Code: 1017

Dragon's Head
Code: 1018

Sorceress
Code: 1019

Castle
Code: 1020

Grim Reaper
Code: 1021

Skull with Snake
Code: 1022

Wizard in Moon
Code: 1023

Sun Dragon
Code: 1024

Reborn Dragon
Code: 1025

Curled Dragon
Code: 1026

LARGE ROUND PENDANTS

ISSUED: 1992/3
ISSUE PRICE: £6.95
CURRENT PRICE: £6.95

Wizard
Code: 1001

Dragon
Code: 1002

Unicorn
Code: 1003

Pegasus
Code: 1004

Dragon on Tower
Code: 2484
Scheduled for retirement: 31st December 1994

Wizard in Window
Code: 2485
Scheduled for retirement: 31st December 1994

Small Unicorn
Code: 2486
Scheduled for retirement: 31st December 1994

Dragon and Skulls
Code: 2487
Scheduled for retirement: 31st December 1994

Wizard and Damsels
Code: 2488
Scheduled for retirement: 31st December 1994

Unicorn
Code: 2489
Scheduled for retirement:
31st December 1994

Pegasus
Code: 2490
Scheduled for retirement:
31st December 1994

Pegasus and Girl
Code: 2491
Scheduled for retirement:
31st December 1994

LARGE PENDANTS

ISSUED: 1992/3
ISSUE PRICE: £4.65
CURRENT PRICE: £4.70

Unicorn
Code: 2400

Pegasus
Code: 2401

Wizard's Head
Code: 2402

Dragon's Head
Code: 2403

Sorceress
Code: 2404

Castle
Code: 2405
Scheduled for retirement:
31st December 1994

Grim Reaper
Code: 2406

Skull with Snake
Code: 2407

Wizard in Moon
Code: 2408

Sun Dragon
Code: 2409

Reborn Dragon
Code: 2410

Curled Dragon
Code: 2411
Scheduled for retirement:
31st December 1994

Sitting Dragon
Code: 2424

Wizard of Knowledge
Code: 2425

Intertwined Dragons
Code: 2426

Elf with Lyre
Code: 2427

Dragon in Wings
Code: 2428

Flying Pegasus
Code: 2429

Filigree Wizard
Code: 2430

The Phoenix
Code: 2431

Filigree Unicorn
Code: 2432

Flying Dragon
Code: 2433

Double Dragon
Code: 2434

Circling Dragons
Code: 2435

SMALL ROUND PENDANTS

ISSUED: 1992/3
ISSUE PRICE: £4.65
CURRENT PRICE: £4.70

Wizard
Code: 1005

Dragon
Code: 1006

Unicorn
Code: 1007

Pegasus
Code: 1008

SMALL PENDANTS

ISSUED: 1992/3
ISSUE PRICE: £3.95
CURRENT PRICE: £3.95

Sitting Dragon
Code: 2448

Wizard of Knowledge
Code: 2449

Intertwined Dragons
Code: 2450

Elf with Lyre
Code: 2451

Dragon in Wings
Code: 2452

Flying Pegasus
Code: 2453

Filigree Wizard
Code: 2454

The Phoenix
Code: 2455

Filigree Unicorn
Code: 2456

Flying Dragon
Code: 2457

Double Dragon
Code: 2458

Circling Dragons
Code: 2459

Fairy on Toadstool
Code: 2460

Celtic Symbol
Code: 2461

Baby Dragon
Code: 2462

Face of the Sun
Code: 2463

Snarling Dragon
Code: 2464

Dragon in Flight
Code: 2465

BROOCHES

ISSUED: 1992/3
ISSUE PRICE: £4.65
CURRENT PRICE: £4.70

All brooches are sched-
uled for retirement on
31st December 1994.

Unicorn
Code: 2412

Pegasus
Code: 2413

Wizard's Head
Code: 2414

Dragon's Head
Code: 2415

Sorceress
Code: 2416

Castle
Code: 2417

Grim Reaper
Code: 2418

Skull with Snake
Code: 2419

Wizard in Moon
Code: 2420

Sun Dragon
Code: 2421

Reborn Dragon
Code: 2422

Curled Dragon
Code: 2423

Sitting Dragon
Code: 2436

Wizard of Knowledge
Code: 2437

Intertwined Dragons
Code: 2438

Elf with Lyre Code: 2439

Dragon in Wings
Code: 2440

Flying Pegasus
Code: 2441

Filigree Wizard
Code: 2442

The Phoenix
Code: 2443

Filigree Unicorn
Code: 2444

Flying Dragon
Code: 2445

Double Dragon
Code: 2446

Circling Dragons
Code: 2447

EARRINGS

ISSUED: 1992/3
ISSUE PRICE: £3.95
CURRENT PRICE: £3.95

Sitting Dragon
Code: 2466

Wizard of Knowledge
Code: 2467

Intertwined Dragons
Code: 2468

Elf with Lyre
Code: 2469

Dragon in Wings
Code: 2470

Flying Pegasus
Code: 2471

Filigree Wizard
Code: 2472

The Phoenix
Code: 2473

Filigree Unicorn
Code: 2474

Flying Dragon
Code: 2475

Double Dragon
Code: 2476

Circling Dragons
Code: 2477

Fairy on Toadstool
Code: 2478

Celtic Symbol
Code: 2479

Baby Dragon
Code: 2480

Face of the Sun
Code: 2481

Snarling Dragon
Code: 2482

Dragon in Flight
Code: 2483

PEWTER BELT BUCKLES

ISSUED: 1992/3
ISSUE PRICE: £8.95
CURRENT PRICE: £8.95

All twelve belt buckles are scheduled for retirement on 31st December 1994.

Reborn Dragon
Code: 1028

Dragon's Head
Code: 1029

Wizard's Head
Code: 1030

Dragon on Moon
Code: 1031

Sun
Code: 1032

Cauldron of Light
Code: 1033

Seven Skulls
Code: 1034

Wizard of the Stars
Code: 1035

Dragon of the Sun
Code: 1036

Magical Encounter
Code: 1037

Sitting Dragon
Code: 1038

Pegasus
Code: 1039

Miscellaneous

First Issue/1994 List Prices of Current Studies

L isted here are the first issue prices of all *Myth and Magic* studies, plus Dark Secrets, and the recommended retail prices set for 1994 (List Price). Early mould versions of studies which are still currently available are also listed.

Studies marked with an asterisk (*) also have an early mould version, the value of which is listed in the Secondary Market Price Guide beginning on page 132.

NAME	YEAR OF ISSUE	FIRST ISSUE PRICE £	1994 LIST PRICE £
STANDARD SIZE STUDIES			
INCANTATION *	'89	9.95	14.95
SIREN	'89	9.95	14.95
BOOK OF SPELLS *	'89	9.95	12.50
CAULDRON OF LIGHT *	'89	9.95	12.50
GUARDIAN DRAGON *	'89	9.95	14.95
GRIM REAPER	'89	9.95	14.95
UNICORN *	'89	9.95	12.50
CASTLE OF SOULS *	'89	12.95	19.95
DRAGON GATEWAY *	'89	12.95	19.95
DRAGON RIDER *	'89	9.95	14.95
REBORN DRAGON	'89	9.95	14.95
WIZARD OF LIGHT *	'89	9.95	14.95
PEGASUS *	'89	9.95	14.95
FIRE WIZARD	'90	10.95	14.95
MOTHER NATURE *	'90	10.95	14.95
KEEPER OF THE TREASURE *	'90	10.95	12.50
DRAGON OF THE FOREST	'90	10.95	14.95
DRAGON OF WISDOM *	'90	10.95	14.95
SPIRITS OF THE FOREST	'90	10.95	19.95
WIZARD OF AUTUMN *	'91	12.95	14.95
WIZARD OF WINTER *	'91	12.95	14.95
WIZARD OF SPRING *	'91	12.95	14.95
WIZARD OF SUMMER *	'91	12.95	14.95
DRAGON OF THE MOON *	'91	12.95	14.95
DRAGON OF THE SUN *	'91	12.95	14.95
DRAGON OF THE CLOUDS *	'91	12.95	14.95
SPIRITED PEGASUS	'91	12.95	14.95
MOON WIZARD	'91	12.95	14.95
DRAGON OF THE STARS	'91	17.50	14.95
SORCERESS OF LIGHT	'91	12.95	14.95
JEWELLED DRAGON	'91	12.95	14.95
RUNELORE	'91	17.50	19.95
DRAGON QUEEN	'92	18.95	19.95
ICE DRAGON *	'92	13.95	14.95
SLEEPY DRAGON	'92	13.95	14.95
UNICORN OF LIGHT	'92	13.95	14.95
STARSPELL	'92	13.95	14.95
VISIONARY *	'92	18.95	19.95
CRYSTAL SPELL	'92	13.95	14.95
UNICORN RIDER *	'92	13.95	14.95

NAME	YEAR OF ISSUE '92	FIRST ISSUE PRICE £	1994 LIST PRICE £
LOREMAKER *	'92	13.95	14.95
DRAGON'S ENCHANTRESS	'92	18.95	19.95
LEAF SPIRIT	'92	13.95	14.95
WIZARD OF THE FUTURE *	'92	13.95	14.95
SWAMP DRAGON	'92	13.95	14.95
DRAGON OF THE SKULLS	'92	13.95	14.95
DARK DRAGON *	'92	13.95	14.95
DRAGON OF LIGHT	'92	13.95	14.95
FOUNTAIN OF LIFE	'93	14.75	14.95
DAWN OF THE DRAGON *	'93	14.75	14.95
DRAGON OF PREHISTORY	'93	14.75	14.95
DEFENDER OF THE CRYSTAL	'93	14.75	14.95
RISING OF THE PHOENIX	'93	14.75	14.95
PROTECTOR OF THE YOUNG	'93	14.75	14.95
UNICORNS OF FREEDOM	'93	14.75	14.95
KEEPER OF THE SKULLS	'93	19.75	19.95
WIZARD OF THE SERPENTS	'93	14.75	14.95
LOVING DRAGONS *	'93	14.75	14.95
SWORD MASTER	'93	14.75	14.95
DRAGON OF MYSTERY *	'93	14.75	14.95
WIZARD OF THE SKIES *	'94	14.95	14.95
DRAGON OF THE TREASURE	'94	14.95	14.95
WIZARD OF THE LAKE	'94	14.95	14.95
BANISHING DRAGON	'94	14.95	14.95
DRAGON'S CASTLE *	'94	14.95	19.95
MYSTICAL TRAVELLER	'94	14.95	14.95
ARMOURED DRAGON *	'94	14.95	14.95
HATCHLINGS *	'94	14.95	14.95
DRAGON OF THE ICE CRYSTALS	'94	17.95	17.95
MISCHIEVOUS DRAGON	'94	14.95	14.95
CRYSTAL UNICORN	'94	17.95	17.95
SUMMONER OF LIGHT	'94	17.95	17.95
MAJESTIC DRAGON	'94	17.95	17.95
PROUD PEGASUS	'94	14.95	14.95
LARGER STUDIES			
DRAGON MASTER	'90	175.00	191.50
MAGICAL ENCOUNTER *	'90	17.95	19.95
KEEPER OF THE MAGIC *	'90	34.95	39.95
MEETING OF THE UNICORNS *	'90	34.95	39.95
VII SEEKERS OF KNOWLEDGE *	'90	175.00	191.50
LE MORTE D'ARTHUR *	'90	49.95	54.50
MAGICAL VISION *	'90	49.95	54.50
ALTAR OF ENLIGHTENMENT *	'91	49.95	54.50
POWER OF THE CRYSTAL	'91	350.00	385.00
AWAKENING	'92	37.95	39.95
CRYSTAL DRAGON	'92	59.95	63.95
GATHERING OF THE UNICORNS *	'92	185.00	191.50
INVOCATION *	'93	49.95	54.50
FIGHTING DRAGONS	'93	39.95	39.95
PLAYFUL DOLPHINS	'93	33.50	33.50
DRAGON OF DARKNESS *	'94	39.95	39.95
DESTROYER OF THE CRYSTAL	'94	49.95	49.95
A TRANQUIL MOMENT	'94	49.95	49.95
GREAT EARTH DRAGON	'94	59.95	59.95

NAME	YEAR OF ISSUE	FIRST ISSUE PRICE £	1994 LIST PRICE £
ONE YEAR ONLY STUDIES			
DRAGON OF THE UNDERWORLD	'94	41.50	41.50
GUARDIAN OF THE CRYSTAL	'95	49.95	NA
EXHIBITION ONLY STUDIES			
VEXIUS	'94	41.50	41.50
COLLECTORS CLUB			
SLEEPY DRAGON	'94	00.00	00.00
CRYSTAL SHIELD	'94	19.95	19.95
BATTLE FOR THE CRYSTAL	'95	To be decided	NA
THE ARTHURIAN LEGEND			
MERLIN	'90	10.95	14.95
EXCALIBUR *	'90	10.95	12.50
CAMELOT *	'90	14.95	19.95
KING ARTHUR *	'90	10.95	14.95
QUEEN GUINEVERE	'90	10.95	14.95
MORGAN LE FEY	'90	14.95	19.95
SIR LANCELOT *	'90	14.95	19.95
VIGIL OF SIR GALAHAD *	'92	18.50	19.95
SIR MORDRED	'92	13.95	14.95
RETURN OF EXCALIBUR *	'92	13.95	14.95
SIR GAWAIN *	'93	14.95	14.95
KING ARTHUR AND SIR BEDEVERE	'93	19.95	19.95
MINIATURES			
Book of Spells	'89	4.95	6.35
Cauldron of Light	'89	4.95	6.35
Winged Serpent	'89	4.95	6.35
Master Wizard	'89	4.95	6.35
Guardian Dragon	'89	4.95	6.35
Unicorn	'89	4.95	6.35
Pegasus	'89	4.95	6.35
Grim Reaper	'90	5.15	6.35
Dragon Gateway	'90	5.15	6.35
Reborn Dragon	'90	5.15	6.35
Fire Dragon	'90	5.15	6.35
Wizard of Light	'90	5.15	6.35
Mother Nature	'91	5.55	6.35
Fire Wizard	'91	5.55	6.35
Dragon of the Lake	'91	5.55	6.35
Merlin	'91	5.55	6.35
Camelot	'91	5.55	6.35
King Arthur	'91	5.55	6.35
Dragon of the Forest	'92	5.95	6.35
Dragon of the Moon	'92	5.95	6.35
Wizard of Winter	'92	5.95	6.35
Dragon of Wisdom	'92	5.95	6.35
Dragon of the Sun	'92	5.95	6.35
Dragon of the Clouds	'92	5.95	6.35
Moon Wizard	'93	6.25	6.35
Unicorn of Light	'93	6.25	6.35
Return of Excalibur	'93	6.25	6.35
Magical Encounter	'93	6.25	6.35
Ice Dragon	'93	6.25	6.35

NAME	YEAR OF ISSUE	FIRST ISSUE PRICE £	1994 LIST PRICE £
Sleepy Dragon	'93	6.25	6.35
Keeper of the Skulls	'94	6.35	6.35
Dark Dragon	'94	6.35	6.35
Protector of the Young	'94	6.35	6.35
Dragon of Light	'94	6.35	6.35
Unicorns of Freedom	'94	6.35	6.35
Defender of the Crystal	'94	6.35	6.35
THE LORD OF THE RINGS COLLECTION			
BILBO BAGGINS	'91	13.95	16.50
GANDALF	'91	24.95	27.50
GOLLUM	'91	17.50	19.95
FRODO BAGGINS	'92	14.95	16.50
BILBO'S TALE	'92	14.95	16.50
GIMLI THE DWARF	'92	14.95	16.50
SAM GAMGEE	'92	14.95	16.50
ARAGORN (STRIDER)	'92	14.95	16.50
AN ORC	'92	17.95	19.95
LEGOLAS THE ELF	'92	17.95	19.95
MIRROR OF GALADRIEL	'92	17.95	19.95
SARUMAN	'92	25.75	27.50
BALROG	'92	39.95	42.50
GANDALF AND SHADOWFAX	'92	39.95	42.50
A BLACK RIDER	'92	39.95	42.50
PIPPIN (PEREGRIN TOOK)	'92	14.95	16.50
MERRY (MERIADOC BRANDYBUCK)	'92	14.95	16.50
BOROMIR	'92	14.95	16.50
TREEBEARD (FANGHORN)	'92	25.75	27.50
DARK SECRETS			
DARK SECRETS	'94	49.95	49.95
GUARDIAN OF THE SKULLS	'94	17.75	17.75
SKULL GATEWAY	'94	19.95	19.95
TORTURED SKULL	'94	19.95	19.95
SERPENT OF THE SKULLS	'94	19.95	19.95
ALTAR OF THE SKULLS	'94	14.95	14.95
SKULL MASTER	'94	19.95	19.95
VAMPIRE OF THE SKULLS	'94	14.95	14.95
CHAMBER OF THE SKULLS	'94	59.95	59.95
GUARDIAN OF THE DEMONS	'94	17.75	17.75
ICE DEMON	'94	14.95	14.95
DEMON OF THE PIT	'94	14.95	14.95
DEMON OF THE KNIGHT	'94	14.95	14.95
DEMON OF THE CATACOMBS	'94	14.95	14.95
DEMON SLAYER	'94	14.95	14.95
DEMON JAILER	'94	14.95	14.95
CHAMBER OF THE DEMONS	'94	59.95	59.95
GUARDIAN OF THE SKELETONS	'94	17.95	17.95
FORGOTTEN SKELETON	'94	17.95	17.95
PRISONER OF THE SWORD	'94	17.95	17.95
VIGIL OF THE SKELETON	'94	14.95	14.95
EXECUTIONER	'94	14.95	14.95
FINDER OF THE TREASURE	'94	14.95	14.95
SKELETON WARRIOR	'94	17.95	17.95
CHAMBER OF THE SKELETONS	'94	59.95	59.95

Secondary Market Price Guide

Listed here are first issue prices, final retail prices (prior to retirement) and current valuations of all retired *Myth and Magic* studies and related collections, plus early mould versions of current studies. Miniatures are included but other miscellaneous items and memorabilia are not; prices for these (current and retired) are given in the section starting on page 113.

It must be stressed that the valuations quoted are intended as a guide only.

Collectors selling to dealers should be prepared to deduct anything from 10% to 50 % from the prices quoted. 40% is probably an acceptable working average.

The secondary market values have been compiled using information from collectors and dealers. Wherever possible we have ignored extreme prices — either high or low — favouring mid-range values. For example, an isolated sale of Quest for the Truth with a Sahara crystal for £1,250 has been documented but is not reflected in this guide.

Valuations are current as at the issue of this Guide. The secondary market is strong currently, if anything the values given should be revised upwards.

Besides the regular factors of supply and demand, other features can affect values — in particular, the size, colour and shape of the crystal on a figurine. The Tudor Mint stopped using cubic crystals, for example, in late 1992, and pieces incorporating a cubic crystal therefore fetch a premium. As a general rule, studies with unusual crystals — conical, cubic, or 'football-shaped' — attract a premium of at least £30 — though exceptions do exist (early Earth Wizards with conical crystals fetch 2 or 3 times the price of a standard study).

Higher prices are paid for studies with their original box. The colour, type and condition of the box is also important to the serious collector. Blue boxes are the most sought after, and add about £25 to values.

Issue prices are also a guide only, and reflect the typical price on issue of a particular model. UK Retail Price Maintenance was abolished some years ago and The Tudor Mint did not issue Retail Price Lists until 1992. Between 1989 and 1991, retailers set their own prices without guidelines.

List Prices of current studies in Mould 2 or 3 versions are on pages 128-131.

NAME	ISSUE PRICE & FINAL PRICE	CURRENT VALUATION		
		Mould 1	Mould 2	Mould 3 (or (2) prototype)
STANDARD SIZE				
INCANTATION	9.95 / NA	125-150	List Price	-
EVIL OF GREED	9.95 / 9.95	150-175	-	-
BOOK OF SPELLS	9.95 / NA	125-150	List Price	-
ENCHANTED CASTLE	9.95 / 12.95	200-250	60-90	-
CAULDRON OF LIGHT	9.95 / NA	200-250	50-75	List Price
WINGED SERPENT	9.95 / 12.95	200-250	50-80	-
WHITE WITCH	9.95 / 12.95	200-250	50-75	-
MASTER WIZARD	9.95 / 14.75	100-150	20-30	-
INFERNAL DEMON	9.95 / 9.95	350-400	175-200	125-175
WARRIOR KNIGHT	9.95 / 10.95	200-250	100-150	-
DEADLY COMBAT	9.95 / 9.95	400-450	250-300	200-250
OLD HAG	9.95 / 10.95	300-350	125-175	-
CRYSTAL QUEEN	9.95 / 14.75	40-50	25-35	-
ASTRONOMER	9.95 / 10.95	300-350	75-105	-
PIPES OF PAN	9.95 / 10.95	100-150	-	-
MISCHIEVOUS GOBLIN	9.95 / 10.95	200-250	80-100	-
GORGON MEDUSA	9.95 / 10.95	125-150	90-125	-
ALCHEMIST	9.95 / 10.95	300-350	75-105	-

NAME	ISSUE PRICE & FINAL PRICE	CURRENT VALUATION Mould 1	Mould 2	Mould 3 (or [2] prototype)
MERMAN	9.95 / 10.95	75-100	65-80	-
GUARDIAN DRAGON	9.95 / NA	35-50	List Price	-
MINOTAUR	9.95 / 10.95	100-150	-	-
UNICORN	9.95 / NA	90-125	List Price	-
CASTLE OF SOULS	12.95 / NA	40-50	List Price	-
DRAGON GATEWAY	12.95 / NA	20-25	List price	-
DRAGON RIDER	9.95 / NA	225-250	50-60	List Price
DRAGON'S KISS	9.95 / 14.75	70-80	25-30	-
WITCH AND FAMILIAR	9.95 /10.95	120-150	-	-
ORIENTAL DRAGON	9.95 / 14.75	130-150	20-30	-
FIRE DRAGON	9.95 / 14.75	20-30	-	-
GIANT SORCEROR	9.95 / 14.75	300-350	20-30	-
WIZARD OF LIGHT	9.95 / NA	85-100	List Price	-
LIGHT OF KNOWLEDGE	9.95 / 10.95	60-80	-	-
PEGASUS	9.95 / NA	50-75	List Price	-
EARTH WIZARD	10.95 / 12.95	50-150 [1]	-	-
WATER WIZARD	10.95 /12.95	50-150 [1]	-	-
AIR WIZARD	10.95 / 12.95	50-150 [1]	-	-
MOTHER NATURE	10.95 / NA	20-25	List Price	-
DRAGON OF THE LAKE	14.95 / 19.75	50-100 [1]	-	-
DRAGON'S SPELL	10.95 / 13.95	50-60	-	-
KEEPER OF THE TREASURE	10.95 / NA	175-200	List Price	-
GEORGE AND THE DRAGON	10.95 /10.95	300-350	-	-
DRAGON OF THE SEA	10.95 /14.75	20-30	-	-
DRAGON OF WISDOM	10.95 / NA	50-100 [1]	List Price	-
VIRGIN AND UNICORN	15.35 /19.75	120-130 [1]	30-40	-
WIZARD OF AUTUMN	12.95 / NA	List Price	-	450-500 [2]
WIZARD OF WINTER	12.95 / NA	50-60	List Price	-
WIZARD OF SPRING	12.95 / NA	40-50	List Price	450-500 [2]
WIZARD OF SUMMER	12.95 / NA	List Price	-	250-275 [2]
DRAGON OF THE MOON	12.95 / NA	List Price	-	500+ [2]
DRAGON OF THE SUN	12.95 / NA	225-250	List Price	500+ [2]
DRAGON OF THE CLOUDS	12.95 / NA	List Price	-	500+ [2]
CASTLE OF SPIRES	17.50 / 19.75	30-40	-	-
CASTLE IN THE CLOUDS	12.95 / 13.95	50-75	-	-
OLD FATHER TIME	17.50 / 19.75	30-40	-	-
FAIRY QUEEN	13.95 / 14.75	25-35	-	-
ICE DRAGON	13.95 / NA	30-40	List Price	-
VISIONARY	18.95 / NA	List Price	-	500+ [2]
UNICORN RIDER	13.95 / NA	50-60	List Price	-
LOREMAKER	13.95 / NA	25-30	List Price	-
WIZARD OF THE FUTURE	13.95 / NA	30-40	List Price	-
DARK DRAGON	13.95 / NA	25-30	List Price	-
DAWN OF THE DRAGON	14.75 / NA	75-85	List Price	-
LOVING DRAGONS	14.75 / NA	40-50	List Price	-
DRAGON OF MYSTERY	14.75 / NA	50-60	40-50	List Price
WIZARD OF THE SKIES	14.95 / NA	30-40	List Price	-
DRAGON'S CASTLE	14.95 / NA	25-30	List Price	-
ARMOURED DRAGON	14.95 / NA	75-90	50-60	List Price
HATCHLINGS	14.95 / NA	100-120	List Price	-
LARGER				
MAGICAL ENCOUNTER	17.95 / NA	40-60	List Price	
KEEPER OF THE MAGIC	34.95 / NA	400-550 [3]	List Price	-
SUMMONING THE ELEMENTS	34.95 / 39.95	275-300	125-175	100-150
SORCEROR'S APPRENTICE	34.95 / 39.95	300-350	200-250	-

NAME	ISSUE PRICE & FINAL PRICE	CURRENT VALUATION Mould 1	Mould 2	Mould 3 (or [2] prototype)
NEST OF DRAGONS	34.95 / 39.95	50-60	-	-
MEETING OF THE UNICORNS	34.95 / NA	100-125 [1]	List Price	-
SENTINELS AT THE PORTAL	34.95 / 39.95	200-250	-	-
VII SEEKERS OF KNOWLEDGE	175.00 / NA	200-225	List Price	-
LE MORTE D'ARTHUR	49.95 / NA	100-125	List Price	-
MAGICAL VISION	49.95 / NA	150-175	List Price	-
DANCE OF THE DOLPHINS	175.00 / NA	200-225	-	-
ALTAR OF ENLIGHTENMENT	49.95 / NA	75-100	List Price	-
GATHERING OF UNICORNS	185.00 / NA	200-225	List Price	-
INVOCATION	49.95 / NA	150-175	List Price	-
DRAGON OF DARKNESS	39.95 / NA	150-175	List Price	-
ARTHURIAN LEGEND				
INTO MERLIN'S CARE	17.95 / 19.75	100-125	20-25	-
EXCALIBUR	10.95 / NA	25-30	List Price	-
CAMELOT	14.95 / NA	40-50	List Price	-
KING ARTHUR	10.95/ NA	100-125 [1]	List Price	-
SIR PERCIVAL AND GRAIL	12.95 / 14.75	100-125	-	-
SIR LANCELOT	14.95 / NA	50-60	30-40	List Price
VIGIL OF SIR GALAHAD	18.50 / NA	25-30	List Price	-
RETURN OF EXCALIBUR	13.95 / NA	50-60	List Price	-
SIR GAWAIN	14.95 / NA	20-30	List Price	-
COLLECTORS CLUB				
PROTECTOR	00.00 / 00.00	250-300	-	-
QUEST FOR TRUTH	49.95 / 49.95	650-800+ [4]	400-450	-
GAME OF STRAX	14.95 / 14.95	325-375	-	-
JOVIAL WIZARD	00.00 / 00.00	150-200	-	-
WELL OF ASPIRATIONS	49.95 / 49.95	400-450	300-325	-
PLAYMATES	16.95 / 16.95	150-175	-	500 + [2]
DRAGON OF DESTINY	00.00 / 00.00	100-150	-	-
FRIENDS	18.95 / 18.95	100-125	-	-
ENCHANTED POOL	49.95 / 49.95	450-500	150-175	-
DRAGON OF METHTINTDOUR	00.00 / 00.00	50-100	-	-
MYSTICAL ENCOUNTER	19.75 / 19.75	50-60	-	-
KEEPER OF DRAGONS	49.95 / 49.95	100-110	70-80	-
ONE YEAR ONLY				
FLYING DRAGON	39.95 / 39.95	200-225	150-175	-
DRAGON OF UNDERWORLD	41.50 / 41.50	150-175	List Price	-
EXTRAVAGANZA				
SAURIA	19.95 / 19.95	400-450	-	-
DEINOS	19.95 / 19.95	350-400	-	-
EXHIBITION				
DACTRIUS	39.95 / 39.95	400-450	200-250	-
MINIATURES				
INCANTATION	4.95 / 5.55	40-60	-	-
ENCHANTED CASTLE	4.95 / 6.25	12-15	-	-
WHITE WITCH	4.95 / 5.55	50-75	-	-
CASTLE OF DREAMS	4.95 / NA	100-150	12-15	-
LIGHT OF KNOWLEDGE	4.95 / 5.55	50-60	-	-
SIREN	4.95 / 4.95	75-100	-	-
CRYSTAL QUEEN	5.15 / 5.95	25-30	-	-
ASTRONOMER	5.15 / 5.15	100-125	-	-

NAME	ISSUE PRICE & FINAL PRICE	CURRENT VALUATION Mould 1	Mould 2	Mould 3 (or [2] prototype)
ALCHEMIST	5.15 / 5.15	100-125	-	-
MINOTAUR	5.15 / 5.55	50-75	-	-
CASTLE OF SOULS	5.15 / 6.25	12-15	-	-
DRAGON RIDER	5.15 / 5.15	75-80	-	-
DRAGON'S KISS	5.15 / 5.95	20-25	-	-
WITCH AND FAMILIAR	5.15 / 5.15	100-150	-	-
ORIENTAL DRAGON	5.15 / 6.25	12-15	-	-
GIANT SORCEROR	5.15 / 5.55	50-60	-	-
KEEPER OF THE TREASURE	5.15 / 5.95	25-30	-	-
OLD HAG	5.15 / 5.15	100-145	-	-
EARTH WIZARD	5.55 / 5.95	25-30	-	-
WATER WIZARD	5.55 / 5.95	25-30	-	-
AIR WIZARD	5.55 / 5.95	25-30	-	-
DRAGON'S SPELL	5.55 / 5.55	45-60	-	-
EXCALIBUR	5.55 / 6.25	12-15	-	-
QUEEN GUINEVERE	5.55 / 6.25	12-15	-	-
HOBBIT COLLECTION				
BILBO BAGGINS (Hobbit backstamp)	13.95 / 15.95	30-40	-	-
GANDALF (Hobbit backstamp)	24.95 / 26.95	45-50	-	-
GOLLUM (Hobbit backstamp)	17.50 / 19.75	45-50	-	-
THORIN OAKENSHIELD	13.95 / 15.25	50-60	-	-
GREAT GOBLIN	13.95 / 15.25	30-40	-	-
BEORN	24.95 / 25.75	75-80	60-70	-
ELVEN KING	17.50 / 18.75	50-60	-	-
SMAUG DRAGON	54.95 / 55.50	75-80	-	-
BARD	13.95 / 15.25	50-60	-	-
GOOD MORNING AT BAG END	39.95 / 39.95	60-75	-	-
MOON LETTERS	54.95 / 55.50	125-150	-	-
FINDING THE 'PRECIOUS'	39.95 / 39.95	75-100	-	-
CAPTURE OF BILBO	39.95 / 39.95	100-125	-	-
RIDDLES IN DARK	32.95 / 34.95	75-100	-	-
ESCAPE FROM THE WARGS	39.95 / 39.95	100-125	-	-
BARRELS OUT OF BOND	39.95 / 39.95	100-125	-	-
COURAGE OF BILBO	32.95 / 34.95	75-100	-	-
PRISONER OF ELVEN KING	39.95 / 39.95	75-100	-	-
ENCHANTED DOOR	54.95 / 55.50	150-175	-	-
WRATH OF BEORN	39.95 / 39.95	100-125	-	-
JOURNEY'S END	39.95 / 39,95	75-100	-	-
TROLL'S CLEARING	147.95 / 147.95	350-450	-	-
BURGLAR STEALS SMAUG'S GREAT CUP	147.95 / 147.95	500+	200-250	-
FAREWELL, KING UNDER MOUNTAIN	147.95 / 147.95	500+	400-450	-

NOTES:

(1) = depending on type of crystal (not actually a mould variation)

(2) = prototype (never released commercially but offered as gifts and prizes)

(3) = single clear crystal £500-550; single blue crystal £400-425; single other crystal £450.

(4) = greenish/gold (Sahara) crystal £800+; blue crystal £650-750.

C h e c k l i s t

A complete reference list of all Myth and Magic studies and related items, excluding jewellery and Dinosaurs. Use the tick boxes to keep check of everything in your collection. Extremely rare items are not included. Within each grouping, items are listed in Code Number order. Retired pieces are in italics.

CODE   TITLE

STANDARD SIZE STUDIES

Code	Title	
3001	THE INCANTATION	❑
3002	THE SIREN	❑
3003	*THE EVIL OF GREED*	❑
3004	THE BOOK OF SPELLS	❑
3005	*THE ENCHANTED CASTLE*	❑
3006	THE CAULDRON OF LIGHT	❑
3007	*THE WINGED SERPENT*	❑
3008	*THE WHITE WITCH*	❑
3009	*THE MASTER WIZARD*	❑
3010	*THE INFERNAL DEMON*	❑
3011	*THE WARRIOR KNIGHT*	❑
3012	*THE DEADLY COMBAT*	❑
3013	*THE OLD HAG*	❑
3014	*THE CRYSTAL QUEEN*	❑
3015	*THE ASTRONOMER*	❑
3016	*PIPES OF PAN*	❑
3017	*THE MISCHIEVOUS GOBLIN*	❑
3018	*THE GORGON MEDUSA*	❑
3019	*THE ALCHEMIST*	❑
3020	*THE MERMAN*	❑
3021	THE GUARDIAN DRAGON	❑
3022	*THE MINOTAUR*	❑
3023	THE GRIM REAPER	❑
3024	THE UNICORN	❑
3025	SEE 3303	
3026	SEE 3302	
3027	THE CASTLE OF SOULS	❑
3028	THE DRAGON GATEWAY	❑
3029	THE DRAGON RIDER	❑
3030	*THE DRAGON'S KISS*	❑
3031	*WITCH AND FAMILIAR*	❑
3032	*THE ORIENTAL DRAGON*	❑
3033	THE REBORN DRAGON	❑
3034	*THE FIRE DRAGON*	❑
3035	*THE GIANT SORCEROR*	❑
3036	THE WIZARD OF LIGHT	❑
3037	*THE LIGHT OF KNOWLEDGE*	❑

CODE   TITLE

Code	Title	
3038	PEGASUS	❑
3039	*THE EARTH WIZARD*	❑
3040	THE FIRE WIZARD	❑
3041	*THE WATER WIZARD*	❑
3042	*THE AIR WIZARD*	❑
3043	MOTHER NATURE	❑
3044	*THE DRAGON OF THE LAKE*	❑
3045	*THE DRAGON'S SPELL*	❑
3046	THE KEEPER OF THE TREASURE	❑
3047	*GEORGE AND THE DRAGON*	❑
3048	*THE DRAGON OF THE SEA*	❑
3049	THE DRAGON OF THE FOREST	❑
3050	THE DRAGON OF WISDOM	❑
3051	SPIRITS OF THE FOREST	❑
3052	*VIRGIN AND UNICORN*	❑
3053	THE WIZARD OF AUTUMN	❑
3054	THE WIZARD OF WINTER	❑
3055	THE WIZARD OF SPRING	❑
3056	THE WIZARD OF SUMMER	❑
3057	THE DRAGON OF THE MOON	❑
3058	THE DRAGON OF THE SUN	❑
3059	THE DRAGON OF THE CLOUDS	❑
3060	THE SPIRITED PEGASUS	❑
3061	*THE CASTLE OF SPIRES*	❑
3062	*THE CASTLE IN THE CLOUDS*	❑
3063	THE MOON WIZARD	❑
3064	THE DRAGON OF THE STARS	❑
3065	THE SORCERESS OF LIGHT	❑
3066	THE JEWELLED DRAGON	❑
3067	*OLD FATHER TIME*	❑
3068	RUNELORE	❑
3069	*THE FAIRY QUEEN*	❑
3070	THE DRAGON QUEEN	❑
3071	THE ICE DRAGON	❑
3072	THE SLEEPY DRAGON	❑
3073	THE UNICORN OF LIGHT	❑
3074	STARSPELL	❑
3075	THE VISIONARY	❑
3076	THE CRYSTAL SPELL	❑

CODE	TITLE	
3077	UNICORN RIDER	❏
3078	THE LOREMAKER	❏
3079	THE DRAGON'S ENCHANTRESS	❏
3080	THE LEAF SPIRIT	❏
3081	THE WIZARD OF THE FUTURE	❏
3082	THE SWAMP DRAGON	❏
3083	THE DRAGON OF THE SKULLS	❏
3084	THE DARK DRAGON	❏
3085	THE DRAGON OF LIGHT	❏
3092	THE FOUNTAIN OF LIFE	❏
3093	THE DAWN OF THE DRAGON	❏
3094	THE DRAGON OF PREHISTORY	❏
3095	THE DEFENDER OF THE CRYSTAL	❏
3096	THE RISING OF THE PHOENIX	❏
3097	THE PROTECTOR OF THE YOUNG	❏
3098	THE UNICORNS OF FREEDOM	❏
3099	THE KEEPER OF THE SKULLS	❏
3100	THE WIZARD OF THE SERPENTS	❏
3101	THE LOVING DRAGONS	❏
3102	THE SWORD MASTER	❏
3103	THE DRAGON OF MYSTERY	❏
3104	THE WIZARD OF THE SKIES	❏
3105	THE DRAGON OF THE TREASURE	❏
3106	THE WIZARD OF THE LAKE	❏
3107	BANISHING THE DRAGON	❏
3108	THE DRAGON'S CASTLE	❏
3109	THE MYSTICAL TRAVELLERS	❏
3110	THE ARMOURED DRAGON	❏
3111	THE HATCHLINGS	❏
3112	THE DRAGON OF THE ICE CRYSTALS	❏
3113	THE MISCHIEVOUS DRAGON	❏
3114	THE CRYSTAL UNICORN	❏
3115	THE SUMMONER OF LIGHT	❏
3116	THE MAJESTIC DRAGON	❏
3117	THE PROUD PEGASUS	❏

LARGER STUDIES

CODE	TITLE	
3300	THE DRAGON MASTER	❏
3301	THE MAGICAL ENCOUNTER	❏
3302	THE KEEPER OF THE MAGIC	❏
3303	SUMMONING THE ELEMENTS	❏
3304	THE SORCEROR'S APPRENTICE	❏
3305	THE NEST OF DRAGONS	❏
3306	MEETING OF THE UNICORNS	❏
3307	SENTINELS AT THE PORTAL	❏
3308	THE VII SEEKERS OF KNOWLEDGE	❏
3309	LE MORTE D'ARTHUR	❏
3310	THE MAGICAL VISION	❏

CODE	TITLE	
3311	THE DANCE OF THE DOLPHINS	❏
3312	THE ALTAR OF ENLIGHTENMENT	❏
3313	THE POWER OF THE CRYSTAL	❏
3314	THE AWAKENING	❏
3315	THE CRYSTAL DRAGON	❏
3318	THE GATHERING OF THE UNICORNS	❏
3319	THE INVOCATION	❏
3320	THE FIGHTING DRAGONS	❏
3321	THE PLAYFUL DOLPHINS	❏
3322	THE DRAGON OF DARKNESS	❏
3323	THE DESTROYER OF THE CRYSTAL	❏
3324	A TRANQUIL MOMENT	❏
3325	THE GREAT EARTH DRAGON	❏

ONE YEAR ONLY PIECES

OY93	THE FLYING DRAGON	❏
OY94	THE DRAGON OF THE UNDERWORLD	❏
OY95	THE GUARDIAN OF THE CRYSTAL	❏

EXTRAVAGANZA STUDIES

3600	SAURIA	❏
3602	DEINOS	❏
3604	LITHIA	❏

EXHIBITION ONLY STUDIES

3601	DACTRIUS	❏
3603	VEXIUS	❏

COLLECTORS CLUB STUDIES

1990/91		
CCO1	THE PROTECTOR	❏
9001	THE QUEST FOR THE TRUTH	❏
9002	THE GAME OF STRAX	❏
1991/92		
CCO2	THE JOVIAL WIZARD	❏
9003	THE WELL OF ASPIRATIONS	❏
9004	PLAYMATES	❏
1992/93		
CCO3	THE DRAGON OF DESTINY	❏
9005	FRIENDS	❏
9006	THE ENCHANTED POOL	❏
1993/94		
CCO4	DRAGON OF METHTINTDOUR	❏
9007	THE MYSTICAL ENCOUNTER	❏

CODE	TITLE	
9008	*KEEPER OF THE DRAGONS*	❏
1994/95		
CCO5	THE DREAMY DRAGON	❏
9009	THE CRYSTAL SHIELD	❏
9010	THE BATTLE FOR THE CRYSTAL	❏

THE ARTHURIAN LEGEND

3200	MERLIN	❏
3201	*INTO MERLIN'S CARE*	❏
3202	EXCALIBUR	❏
3203	CAMELOT	❏
3204	KING ARTHUR	❏
3205	QUEEN GUINEVERE	❏
3206	*SIR PERCIVAL AND THE GRAIL*	❏
3207	MORGAN LE FEY	❏
3208	SIR LANCELOT	❏
3209	VIGIL OF SIR GALAHAD	❏
3210	SIR MORDRED	❏
3211	RETURN OF EXCALIBUR	❏
3212	SIR GAWAIN	❏
3213	KING ARTHUR AND SIR BEDEVERE	❏

MISCELLANEOUS

BOOK
4100	THE STRACYL OF UNITY	❏

CRYSTAL KEEPERS
4301	*UNICORN AND DAMSEL*	❏
4302	*DRAGON AND WARRIOR*	❏
4303	*SLEEPING DRAGON*	❏
4304	*FIRE WIZARD*	❏

CHESS SETS
4305	*FANTASY CHESS SET*	❏
4323	TUDOR MINT CHESS SET	❏

PAPER KNIVES
3086	UNICORN	❏
3087	CASTLE	❏
3088	SKULLS	❏
3089	PEGASUS	❏
3090	WIZARD	❏
3091	DRAGON	❏

MINIATURES
3500	*The Incantation*	❏
3501	The Book of Spells	❏
3502	*The Enchanted Castle*	❏
3503	The Cauldron of Light	❏
3504	The Winged Serpent	❏
3505	*The White Witch*	❏

CODE	TITLE	
3506	The Master Wizard	❏
3507	The Guardian Dragon	❏
3508	The Unicorn	❏
3509	Pegasus	❏
3510	*The Castle of Dreams*	❏
3511	*The Light of Knowledge*	❏
3512	*The Siren*	❏
3513	*The Crystal Queen*	❏
3514	*The Astronomer*	❏
3515	*The Alchemist*	❏
3516	*The Minotaur*	❏
3517	The Grim Reaper	❏
3518	*The Castle of Souls*	❏
3519	The Dragon Gateway	❏
3520	*The Dragon Rider*	❏
3521	*The Dragon's Kiss*	❏
3522	*The Witch and Familiar*	❏
3523	*The Oriental Dragon*	❏
3524	The Reborn Dragon	❏
3525	The Fire Dragon	❏
3526	*The Giant Sorceror*	❏
3527	The Wizard of Light	❏
3528	*The Keeper of the Treasure*	❏
3529	*The Old Hag*	❏
3530	Mother Nature	❏
3531	*The Earth Wizard*	❏
3532	The Fire Wizard	❏
3533	*The Water Wizard*	❏
3534	*The Air Wizard*	❏
3535	The Dragon of the Lake	❏
3536	*The Dragon's Spell*	❏
3537	Merlin	❏
3538	*Excalibur*	❏
3539	Camelot	❏
3540	King Arthur	❏
3541	*Queen Guinevere*	❏
3542	Dragon of the Forest	❏
3543	Dragon of the Moon	❏
3544	Wizard of Winter	❏
3545	Dragon of Wisdom	❏
3546	Dragon of the Sun	❏
3547	Dragon of the Clouds	❏
3548	Moon Wizard	❏
3549	Unicorn of Light	❏
3550	Return of Excalibur	❏
3551	Magical Encounter	❏
3552	Ice Dragon	❏
3553	Sleepy Dragon	❏
3554	The Keeper of the Skulls	❏
3555	The Dark Dragon	❏
3556	The Protector of the Young	❏

CODE	TITLE	
3557	The Dragon of Light	❑
3558	The Unicorns of Freedom	❑
3559	The Defender of the Crystal	❑

THE HOBBIT COLLECTION

CODE	TITLE	
5001	*BILBO BAGGINS*	❑
5002	*GANDALF*	❑
5003	*THORIN OAKENSHIELD*	❑
5004	*THE GREAT GOBLIN*	❑
5005	*GOLLUM*	❑
5006	*BEORN*	❑
5007	*THE ELVEN KING*	❑
5008	*SMAUG THE DRAGON*	❑
5009	*BARD*	❑
5010	*'GOOD MORNING' AT BAG END*	❑
5011	*MOON LETTERS*	❑
5012	*FINDING THE 'PRECIOUS'*	❑
5013	*THE CAPTURE OF BILBO*	❑
5014	*'RIDDLES IN THE DARK'*	❑
5015	*ESCAPE FROM THE WARGS*	❑
5016	*BARRELS OUT OF BOND*	❑
5017	*'THE COURAGE OF BILBO'*	❑
5018	*PRISONER OF THE ELVEN KING*	❑
5019	*THE ENCHANTED DOOR*	❑
5020	*THE WRATH OF BEORN*	❑
5021	*JOURNEY'S END*	❑
5022	*THE TROLL'S CLEARING*	❑
5023	*THE BURGLAR STEALS SMAUG'S GREAT CUP*	❑
5024	*FAREWELL, KING UNDER THE MOUNTAIN*	❑

THE LORD OF THE RINGS COLLECTION

CODE	TITLE	
5001	BILBO BAGGINS*	❑
5002	GANDALF*	❑
5005	GOLLUM*	❑
5025	FRODO BAGGINS	❑
5026	BILBO'S TALE	❑
5027	GIMLI THE DWARF	❑
5028	SAM GAMGEE	❑
5029	ARAGORN (STRIDER)	❑
5030	AN ORC	❑
5031	LEGOLAS THE ELF	❑
5032	THE MIRROR OF GALADRIEL	❑
5033	SARUMAN	❑
5034	THE BALROG	❑
5035	GANDALF AND SHADOWFAX	❑
5036	A BLACK RIDER	❑
5037	PIPPIN (PEREGRIN TOOK)	❑

CODE	TITLE	
5038	MERRY (MERIADOC BRANDYBUCK)	❑
5039	BOROMIR	❑
5040	TREEBEARD (FANGHORN)	❑
	* With Lord of the Rings baseplate	

DARK SECRETS

CODE	TITLE	
6201	DARK SECRETS	❑
6202	THE GUARDIAN OF THE SKULLS	❑
6203	THE SKULL GATEWAY	❑
6304	THE TORTURED SKULL	❑
6205	THE SERPENT OF THE SKULLS	❑
6206	THE ALTAR OF THE SKULLS	❑
6207	THE SKULL MASTER	❑
6208	THE VAMPIRE OF THE SKULLS	❑
6209	THE CHAMBER OF THE SKULLS	❑
6210	THE GUARDIAN OF THE DEMONS	❑
6211	THE ICE DEMON	❑
6212	THE DEMON OF THE PIT	❑
6213	THE DEMON OF THE NIGHT	❑
6214	THE DEMON OF THE CATACOMBS	❑
6215	THE DEMON SLAYER	❑
6216	THE DEMON JAILER	❑
6217	THE CHAMBER OF THE DEMONS	❑
6218	THE GUARDIAN OF THE SKELETONS	❑
6219	THE VIGIL OF THE SKELETON	❑
6220	THE FORGOTTEN SKELETON	❑
6221	THE PRISONER OF THE SWORD	❑
6222	THE EXECUTIONER	❑
6223	THE FINDER OF THE TREASURE	❑
6224	THE SKELETON WARRIOR	❑
6225	THE CHAMBER OF THE SKELETONS	❑

Some Useful Addresses

Membership of the Myth and Magic Collectors Club is now available worldwide. Application forms can be picked up from any nominated stockist and should be returned (with the appropriate payment) to one of the following addresses:

MYTH AND MAGIC COLLECTORS CLUB

CANADA

Myth and Magic Collectors Club (Canadian Division), 55-E East Beaver Creek Road, Richmond Hill, Ontario, L4B 1EB
Telephone: (905) 731 3232
Fax: (905) 731 0872

UK, EUROPE & REST OF THE WORLD

The Myth and Magic Collectors Club, Vulcan Road, Solihull, West Midlands B91 2JY, England
Telephone: (0121) 711 4128
Fax: (0121) 711 1086

Correspondence with the Editor of The Methtintdour Times is always welcome and should be sent to the Solihull address in England.

THE TOLKIEN SOCIETY

Those who wish to learn more about J.R.R. Tolkien and his remarkable work can do no better than to join the society which bears his name.

THE TOLKIEN SOCIETY,
Flat 5, 357 High Street, Cheltenham, Gloucestershire GL50 3HT.

PERIODICALS

For buying and selling studies, the following magazines and newspapers are well established as a means of reaching dealers or placing classified advertisements.

EXCHANGE & MART
Link House, 25 West Street, Poole, Dorset (England)
Telephone: (0202) 671171
Used by collectors and dealers in the UK to buy and sell just about anything you care to name, including collectables.

COLLECTORS NEWS
17 Clare Avenue, Woodbridge, Suffolk IP12 4ES (England)
Bi-monthly, includes ads for dealers in collectables.

CANADIAN COLLECTIBLES
(Formerly 'Insight on Collectibles')
103 Lakeshore Road Suite 262, St Catherines, Ontario L2N 2T6 (Canada)
Canada's only collectables publication.

COLLECTORS MART
650 Westdale Drive, Wichita, Kansas 67209 (USA)
Bimonthly, dedicated to collectibles. Has a regular classified section featuring ads for dealers, including many secondary market listings.

Index of Studies

THE AIR WIZARD 59
THE ALCHEMIST 56
THE ALTAR OF ENLIGHTENMENT 45
THE ALTAR OF THE SKULLS 99
ARAGORN (STRIDER) 89
THE ARMOURED DRAGON 38
THE ASTRONOMER 54
THE AWAKENING 46
THE BALROG 91
BANISHING THE DRAGON 37
BARD 83
BARRELS OUT OF BOND 84
THE BATTLE FOR THE CRYSTAL 73
BEORN 82
BILBO BAGGINS 81
BILBO'S TALE THE AIR WIZARD 88
A BLACK RIDER 91
THE BOOK OF SPELLS 19
BOROMIR 92
THE BURGLAR STEALS SMAUG'S
   GREAT CUP 87
CAMELOT 94
THE CAPTURE OF BILBO 84
THE CASTLE IN THE CLOUDS 62
THE CASTLE OF SOULS 20
THE CASTLE OF SPIRES 61
THE CAULDRON OF LIGHT 19, 109
THE CHAMBER OF THE DEMONS 102
THE CHAMBER OF THE SKELETONS 105
THE CHAMBER OF THE SKULLS 100
CHESS SETS 113
'THE COURAGE OF BILBO' 85
CRYSTAL KEEPERS 120
THE CRYSTAL DRAGON 46
THE CRYSTAL QUEEN 54
THE CRYSTAL SHIELD 73
THE CRYSTAL SPELL 30
THE CRYSTAL UNICORN 39
DACTRIUS 79

THE DANCE OF THE DOLPHINS 66
THE DARK DRAGON 32
DARK SECRETS 98
THE DAWN OF THE DRAGON 33
THE DEADLY COMBAT 53
THE DEFENDER OF THE CRYSTAL 33
DEINOS 78
THE DEMON JAILER 102
THE DEMON OF THE CATACOMBS 102
THE DEMON OF THE NIGHT 101
THE DEMON OF THE PIT 101
THE DEMON SLAYER 102
THE DESTROYER OF THE CRYSTAL 49
DINOSAURS 121
THE DRAGON GATEWAY 20
THE DRAGON MASTER 41
THE DRAGON OF DARKNESS 49
THE DRAGON OF DESTINY 69
THE DRAGON OF LIGHT 32
THE DRAGON OF METHTINTDOUR 69
THE DRAGON OF MYSTERY 36
THE DRAGON OF PREHISTORY 33
THE DRAGON OF THE CLOUDS 26, 106
THE DRAGON OF THE FOREST 23
THE DRAGON OF THE ICE
   CRYSTALS 38
THE DRAGON OF THE LAKE 12, 60
THE DRAGON OF THE MOON 15, 25
THE DRAGON OF THE MOUNTAINS 106
THE DRAGON OF THE SEA 61
THE DRAGON OF THE SKULLS 32
THE DRAGON OF THE STARS 27
THE DRAGON OF THE TREASURE 36
THE DRAGON OF THE
   UNDERWORLD 76, 109
THE DRAGON OF WISDOM 23
THE DRAGON QUEEN 28
THE DRAGON RIDER 21, 111
THE DRAGON'S CASTLE 37

THE DRAGON'S ENCHANTRESS	31	THE GUARDIAN OF THE SKELETONS		103
THE DRAGON'S KISS	57	THE GUARDIAN OF THE SKULLS		98
THE DRAGON'S SPELL	11, 60	THE HATCHLINGS		38
THE DREAMY DRAGON	70	THE ICE DEMON		101
THE EARTH WIZARD	59	THE ICE DRAGON		28
THE ELVEN KING	82	THE INCANTATION		18, 107
THE ENCHANTED CASTLE	51	THE INFERNAL DEMON	12, 52, 110
THE ENCHANTED DOOR	85	INTO MERLIN'S CARE		93
THE ENCHANTED POOL	71	THE INVOCATION		47, 107
ESCAPE FROM THE WARGS	84	THE JEWELLED DRAGON		27
THE EVIL OF GREED	51	JOURNEY'S END		86
EXCALIBUR	94	THE JOVIAL WIZARD		69
THE EXECUTIONER	104	KEEPER OF THE DRAGONS		73
THE FAIRY QUEEN	62	THE KEEPER OF THE MAGIC		42
FAREWELL, KING UNDER THE		THE KEEPER OF THE SKULLS		35
MOUNTAIN	87	THE KEEPER OF THE TREASURE	23, 108
THE FIGHTING DRAGONS	48	KING ARTHUR		94
FIGHT FOR FREEDOM	112	KING ARTHUR AND SIR BEDEVERE		97
THE FINDER OF THE TREASURE	104	THE LEAF SPIRIT		31
FINDING THE 'PRECIOUS'	84	LEGOLAS THE ELF		90
THE FIRE DRAGON	58	LE MORTE D'ARTHUR		44
THE FIRE WIZARD	22	THE LIGHT OF KNOWLEDGE		58
THE FLYING DRAGON	75	LITHIA		78
THE FORGOTTEN SKELETON	103	THE LOREMAKER		30
THE FOUNTAIN OF LIFE	32	THE LOVING DRAGONS		35
FRIENDS	72	THE MAGICAL ENCOUNTER		42
FRODO BAGGINS	88	THE MAGICAL VISION		44
THE GAME OF STRAX	71	THE MAJESTIC DRAGON		40
GANDALF	81	THE MASTER WIZARD		52
GANDALF AND SHADOWFAX	91	MEETING OF THE UNICORNS		43
THE GATHERING OF THE		MERLIN		93
UNICORNS	47	THE MERMAN		56
GEORGE AND THE DRAGON	60	MERRY (MERIADOC BRANDYBUCK)		92
THE GIANT SORCEROR	58, 110	MINIATURES		115
GIMLI THE DWARF	88	THE MINOTAUR		56
GOLLUM	82	THE MIRROR OF GALADRIEL		90
'GOOD MORNING' AT BAG END	83	THE MISCHIEVOUS DRAGON		39
THE GORGON MEDUSA	55	THE MISCHIEVOUS GOBLIN		55
THE GREAT EARTH DRAGON	50	MOON LETTERS		83
THE GREAT GOBLIN	82	THE MOON WIZARD		27
THE GRIM REAPER	20	MORGAN LE FEY		95
THE GUARDIAN DRAGON	19	MOTHER NATURE		22
THE GUARDIAN OF THE CRYSTAL	76	THE MYSTICAL ENCOUNTER		72
THE GUARDIAN OF THE DEMONS	101	THE MYSTICAL TRAVELLER		37

THE NEST OF DRAGONS 64
OLD FATHER TIME 62
THE OLD HAG 54
AN ORC 89
THE ORIENTAL DRAGON 57
PAPER KNIVES 114
PEGASUS 22
PIPES OF PAN 55
PIPPIN (PEREGRIN TOOK) 92
THE PLAYFUL DOLPHINS 48
PLAYMATES 71
THE POWER OF THE CRYSTAL 45
PRISONER OF THE ELVEN KING 85
THE PRISONERS OF THE SWORD 104
THE PROTECTOR 68
THE PROTECTOR OF THE YOUNG 34
THE PROUD PEGASUS 40
QUEEN GUINEVERE 95
THE QUEST FOR THE TRUTH 70
THE REBORN DRAGON 21
RETURN OF EXCALIBUR 97
'RIDDLES IN THE DARK' 84
THE RISING OF THE PHOENIX 34
RUNELORE 28
SAM GAMGEE 89
SARUMAN 90
SAURIA 14, 77
SENTINELS AT THE PORTAL 65
THE SERPENTS OF THE SKULLS 99
THE SIREN 18, 107
SIR GAWAIN 97
SIR LANCELOT 96
SIR MORDRED 96
SIR PERCIVAL AND THE GRAIL 95
THE SKELETON WARRIOR 105
THE SKULL MASTER 100
THE SKULL GATEWAY 99
THE SLEEPY DRAGON 28
SMAUG THE DRAGON 83
THE SORCERESS OF LIGHT 27
THE SORCEROR'S APPRENTICE 64, 107, 108
THE SPIRITED PEGASUS 26
SPIRITS OF THE FOREST 24
STARSPELL 29

THE SUMMONER OF LIGHT 39
SUMMONING THE ELEMENTS 63
THE SUN DRAGON 26
THE SWORD MASTER 36
THE SWAMP DRAGON 31
THORIN OAKENSHIELD 82
THE TORTURED SKULL 99
A TRANQUIL MOMENT 50
TREEBEARD (FANGORN) 92
THE TROLL'S CLEARING 86
THE UNICORN 20
UNICORN RIDER 30
THE UNICORNS OF FREEDOM 34
THE UNICORN OF LIGHT 29
THE VAMPIRE OF THE SKULLS 100
VEXIUS 80
VIGIL OF SIR GALAHAD 96
THE VIGIL OF THE SKELETON 103
THE VII SEEKERS OF KNOWLEDGE 43
VIRGIN AND UNICORN 61
THE VISIONARY 29
THE WARRIOR KNIGHT 53
THE WATER WIZARD 59, 111
THE WELL OF ASPIRATIONS 71
THE WHITE WITCH 52
THE WINGED SERPENT 52, 110
THE WITCH AND FAMILIAR 57
THE WIZARD OF AUTUMN 24
THE WIZARD OF THE FUTURE 31
THE WIZARD OF THE LAKE 37
THE WIZARD OF THE SERPENTS 35
THE WIZARD OF THE SKIES 36
THE WIZARD OF LIGHT 21
THE WIZARD OF SPRING 25
THE WIZARD OF SUMMER 25
THE WIZARD OF WINTER 24
THE WRATH OF BEORN 85
ZEUS 112